ELECTRONIC MUSICAL INSTRUMENTS

Hedgehog, in the house

By Norman H. Crowhurst

TAB BOOKS
BLUE RIDGE SUMMIT, PA. 17214

FIRST EDITION

FIRST PRINTING — JANUARY 1971
SECOND PRINTING — FEBRUARY 1972

Copyright © 1971 by TAB BOOKS

Printed in the United States
of America

Library of Congress Card Number: 70-133801

Preface

We are living in a rapidly changing world, a statement quite obvious to the observer of technology. But there is one thing the individual wrapped up in his technological world may have overlooked: the change in music. Yes, the world of music has been changing at an unprecedented rate, too. So in this book we attempt to cover the convergence of two of the most rapidly advancing fields in today's world. And that is a challenge for the author and the reader alike. And it's apparent that the challenge interests you, because you picked up this book.

Challenge is what, in any age, has brought out the best in men. Misapplied, someone may validly observe, it can also bring out the worst, although that may be a matter of viewpoint. However, it is generally conceded that broadening of an individual's horizons is good. The mad scientist is one whose field of vision has become too narrow. So the bringing together of science and art, in such sophisticated form as the various developments going on in electronic music must result in an enlarging of horizons for those who participate.

To participate, you may be a musician, an electronic engineer, or a technician serving, in one way or another, the creative genii who produce the latest masterpieces in music. Whichever you are, this book should help put this wonderful new world into perspective.

Norman H. Crowhurst.

Contents

Chapter 1

Electronics & Music

Of necessity we must deal with both electronics and music, because the two are inseparable in electronic music. For a musical instrument to qualify as electronic, it must at least have some electronic parts in it. Electronic musical instruments, basically, vary all the way from conventional, traditional instruments, to which electronic amplification has been added, to an instrument which contains nothing but electronic parts.

Conversely, for an electronic instrument to be musical, it must produce sound that, whether it resembles traditional musical instruments or not, is acceptable as providing a legitimate musical form, capable of being applied to musical composition or rendition. Opinions may sometimes differ as to whether the result achieved is always musical, but in its most basic sense, this premise is sound.

A study of traditional musical instruments reveals that every instrument comprises three parts: a tone generator, a tone modifier, and an amplifier. Review this with reference to the main classes of instruments that have come down to us.

STRINGS

Typical stringed instruments are the violin, guitar, and piano. Each uses a vibrating string as a tone generator, but each produces a variety of differing sounds based on the design of the other two parts of the instrument. If you think the vibrating string generates the whole sound, try playing an electric guitar (one of those with a solid wood body) and see how much sound it gives without the amplifier switched on.

Also, the method of selecting the pitch of the note played varies. In the piano the strings are pretuned to the pitch they will give every time they are played. With the violin each string is separately tuned to a base pitch, above which it may also be played by appropriate fingering. The same is true of

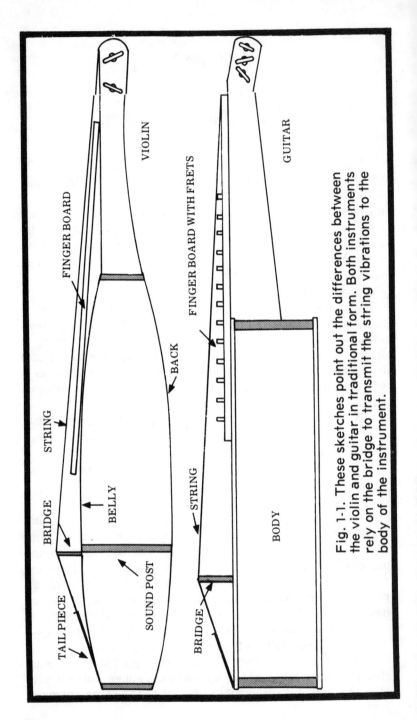

Fig. 1-1. These sketches point out the differences between the violin and guitar in traditional form. Both instruments rely on the bridge to transmit the string vibrations to the body of the instrument.

VIOLIN

FINGER BOARD

STRING

BRIDGE

BELLY

BACK

SOUND POST

TAIL PIECE

GUITAR

FINGER BOARD WITH FRETS

STRING

BRIDGE

BODY

8

the guitar, except that frets across the fingerboard behind the strings make the precise pitch of each note played more definitely identified than in the violin (Fig. 1-1).

Not so commonly recognized is the fact that each string-type generator also possesses tone modifiers. On the piano the loud and soft pedals modify the kind of tone generated by the string, and some pianos a third pedal that provides an additional effect by moving the hammers so they strike only one string instead of the three strings normally tuned in unison. The so-called loud pedal removes the check action, a pad that returns to damp the vibrations whenever a key is released, and the soft pedal usually applies a damping pad constantly to the strings when it is pressed to give the notes a muted quality. And on any piano the player's touch exerts considerable effect on the tone.

The tonal quality of a violin can be varied by the manner of bowing the notes or by plucking them instead. On the guitar the vigor with which the strings are plucked also lends variety of quality to individual tones.

Each of these instruments also has an acoustic amplifier. In the piano, the vibrations of the strings are conveyed to a sound board, usually as large as the instrument itself, from which the sound we hear actually radiates. In a grand piano the sound board is horizontal and sound waves emanate from above (when the lid is open) and below. In an upright the sound board is vertical and the back is open, except for a light, acoustically transparent covering. Some pianos, intended for electronic amplification, have been constructed without any sound boards. If they are played without the amplifier switched on, you can hardly hear them.

Violins and guitars both have a bridge which communicates the vibrations to the belly of the instrument, causing it to vibrate at the same frequency as the string. The belly is one side of a large, hollow cavity with holes often shaped like a letter "f"; that's why they're called "f-holes." The f-holes tune the interior of the instrument which makes up a resonant cavity from which sound radiates through the holes. Sound also radiates from the vibrating "shell" or body of the instrument.

WOODWINDS

In most wind instruments the functions are not so demonstrably separate as they are with strings, but they are there, though they may overlap somewhat. In the woodwinds, such as the clarinet, oboe, bassoon, and the saxophone, the tone generator is a vibrating reed. However, the frequency at which it vibrates, as well as some of the amplification, is determined by the tuning of the pipe beyond the reed. This is usually accomplished with valves that cover and uncover holes in the pipe according to the player's finger movements.

Slightly more amplification is achieved by the bell of the instrument but, being less defined than the bell of brass instruments, the amplification contributed by the bell of a woodwind is not so great. The tone can be modified, also, by the way the player manipulates the reed, the force of the air, and the lip pressure.

BRASS

With the brass wind instruments, such as the trumpet, trombone, and the french horn, the player's lips constitute the tone generator and part of the tone modifier. The length of pipe, coupled with the way it is blown, control the pitch and part of the amplification.

Brass instruments are tuned by changing the length of the pipe. All except the trombone use three valves that bring extra length of pipe into action. The trombone varies the total length quite obviously, by use of its slide. A bugle has no valves, and the different notes are obtained solely by blowing so that different overtones are selected.

A horn can be blown to play its fundamental frequency, for which its length is a half wavelength, or any of its harmonics, for which the same length is an integral number of half wavelengths. Thus a horn tuned to a C of 125 Hz will play the following notes (frequencies) as the blowing is changed: C (125 Hz), C (250 Hz), G (375 Hz), C (500 Hz), E (625 Hz), G (750 Hz), B-flat (875 Hz), C (1,000 Hz). The frequencies in parenthesis are exact harmonics rather than the correct tempered-scale frequencies which would differ slightly.

A good player can modify the note played slightly, enough to come very close to true tempered pitch, by modifying the way he fits his lips to the mouthpiece, called intonation. Table 1-1 lists this same sequence of frequencies with the harmonic frequencies and the corresponding true tempered pitch frequencies. Notice that the frequencies used are not modern concert pitch for either C or B-flat tuning but are chosen for their simple numercial relationship.

10

HARMONIC	NOTE	FREQUENCY	TEMPERED
F(1)	C	125	125
2	C	250	250
3	G	375	374
4	C	500	500
5	E	625	630
6	G	750	749
7	B-flat	875	891
8	C	1000	1000

Table 1-1. Relationship between harmonics and true tempered pitch frequencies.

In the trumpet family of instruments, the valves lengthen the horn as follows: middle valve by one semitone, first valve by two semitones, first two valves by three semitones, last two valves by four semitones, first and last valve by five semitones and all three valves by six semitones. This is a compromise, because the linear increase in length per semitone varies over the 6-semitone range. To show the nature of the compromise, and using percentages of the starting length to the nearest 1 percent, Table 1-2 shows the way a scale of notes is achieved and the natural frequencies produced, alongside the correct tempered scale to correspond, for the middle valve adding 7 percent, the first 13 percent and the third 20 percent of the basic length.

The bell of a brass instrument contributes much more amplification than the bell of a woodwind. Sometimes a mute is used at the bell of a brass instrument to further modify the sound generated.

RESONANT REEDS

Not to be confused with the reeds used in woodwinds, which are untuned and controlled by a resonant pipe and the

NOTE	VALVES PRESSED	FREQUENCY	
		NATURAL	TEMPERED
F-sharp	1 2 3	178	177
G	1 3	188	187
G-sharp	2 3	197	199
A	1 2	208	210
B-flat	1	221	223
B	2	233	236
C		250	250
C-sharp	1 2 3	268	265
D	1 3	282	280
E-flat	2 3	295	298
E	1 2	313	315
F	1	332	333
F-sharp	2	350	354

player's lips, are the resonant reeds used in the harmonica and piano accordian. In such instruments, from the acoustic viewpoint, modulation comes after amplification. Air pressure applied to the reed controls volume in two ways: by controlling the amplitude at which the reed vibrates, and by causing the bursts of air which the vibration modulates to have greater or lesser pressure. It is this change in escaping air pressure that constitutes amplification in this type of instrument. The reed's movement works like a valve in the same way that a tube or transistor does in an electrical oscillator.

NOTE	VALVES PRESSED	FREQUENCY	
		NATURAL	TEMPERED
G		375	374
G-sharp	2 3	394	398
A	1 2	417	421
B-flat	1	443	445
B	2	467	472
C		500	500
C-sharp	1 2	520	530
D	1	553	561
E-flat	2	585	595
E		625	630
F	1	665	667
F-sharp	2	700	707
G		750	749

Table 1-2. Notes produced by various trumpet valve combinations.

VIBES

In these instruments a vibrating bar suspended at nodes in its natural vibrating pattern constitutes the tone generator. The sound is usually produced by striking the bars with mallets. In themselves the bars on a vibe generate relatively little sound, but they are mounted over resonant pipes that amplify their individual tones (Fig. 1-2). The tone can be modified by the structure of the mallets or the manner of striking.

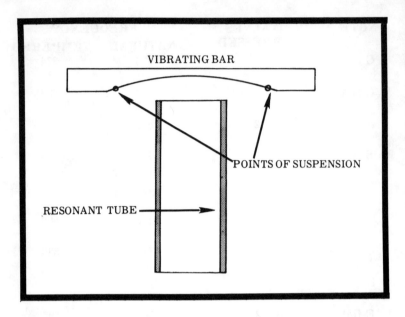

VIBRATING BAR

POINTS OF SUSPENSION

RESONANT TUBE

Fig. 1-2. Cross-section view of the sound generating system used by the vibes group of instruments. The bar is suspended at the correct point to produce the desired pitch. Amplification is provided by the resonant tube.

MUSICAL SAW

This is more of a novelty than a true musical instrument. Actually, any well-tempered carpenter's saw (e.g. cross-cut or rip) will serve. The player usually holds the saw handle tightly between his knees and the tip of the saw lightly between the finger of his left hand. He bends the saw with his left hand, varying the stress by the way he holds it. Sound may be excited by bowing (using a violin bow on the smooth back edge of the saw) or by striking its surface with a soft mallet. The saw vibrates throughout its length at a frequency determined by the stresses set up within it. An amplified sound wave is generated because the vibrating surface is relatively large.

DRUMS

Drums come in two varieties, the open (bongo) and closed types (Fig. 1-3). In each case the diaphragm is the tone generator and the cavity, open or closed, acts as an acoustic amplifier. The sound the drum makes can also be modified by the manner of "exciting" the diaphragm: the kind of drum-stick used (or even a wire brush) and by varying the tension on the diaphragm skin).

The drummer usually has some other accouterments, such as cymbals, blocks, bells, etc. In these the tone generating part and the amplifying part are more definitely integrated, since the vibrating surface of the resonant body itself is large enough to provide acoustic amplification.

TYPES OF SOUND

In modern times another form of distinction has come into prominence. From the point of view we shall pursue later in this book, it could be related to the envelope of the sound. Musically, this describes the way sounds start and sometimes also how they stop. In the broadest distinction, the contrast is between percussive and nonpercussive, or steady tone. The piano, plucked strings, vibes, and all the drummer's

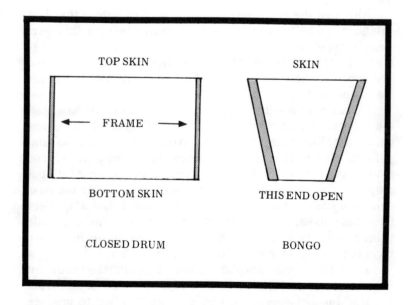

Fig. 1-3. These drawings represent the two basic types of drum, each of which comes in a range of sizes.

prerequisites are classified as percussion, because such sounds are started suddenly, and die away gradually.

If the decay or die-away of the tone is also fairly sudden, rather than sustained, it is called pizzicato, which effect is still in the broader category called percussive. All forms of wind instruments, and strings when bowed, or otherwise stimulated into a steady state of vibration, as opposed to being plucked, are nonpercussive, or steady state.

THE ELECTRONIC CONTRIBUTION

Having thus briefly outlined some types of traditional musical instruments and the way they make their musical sounds, we turn to the "electronification" of musical instruments. Electronics integration varies widely from the addition of amplification to instruments that are still basically a traditional type, through the addition of tone modifiers to essentially a traditional type, then into types where part of the traditional acoustic functions are discarded and replaced by electronics, and, finally to electronic synthesis where the entire sound is generated, modified, and amplified by electronic equipment.

Although the electronic organ is strictly within that last category, there are books devoted exclusively to this particular type of instrument. So, while some reference is made to organs, our emphasis is on those types of electronic instruments, like the synthesizer, that depart from the traditional form, which the organ does not.

Virtually every traditional musical instrument has been the subject of electronic amplification. Commonly used are guitar, amplifiers and traditional bass violin and cello amplifiers, also a good number of accordian amplifiers. The traditional violin has been the subject of experiment, but amplification has been accepted generally with only the bass and cello sizes of the instrument. A few woodwind amplifiers have been used, but gained little acceptance. There is little point in amplifying brass, which has enough power in its own right to drown out the rest of the orchestra!

After the simple amplification of traditional instrument forms, come the electric guitars and basses that depart from the traditional pattern and rely on amplification to produce any audible sound at all. We begin to see here much more being done with electronic sound modulation. Work in this area includes electronic vibrato, along with additional effects like "fuzz," and so forth.

The final step is the complete synthesizer that starts from nothing in the purely physical world and creates sound entirely by electronic synthesis. The earliest example (many years ago now) was the Theremin. There have been more recent examples that have achieved limited acceptance, but it wasn't until the advent of solid-state electronics and integrated circuits with miniaturized packaging that synthesizers capable of producing the latest wonders gained much notice.

Now, the synthesizer with its intriguing musical effects has started a second "round" of change. Musicians with conventional instruments want to duplicate some of the sounds they have heard from the synthesizer. While some of the new sounds are totally new, many of them do bear some resemblance to traditional musical sounds and can also be produced by electronically processing the output from such instruments.

The electronically-amplified piano was an early forerunner of the modified traditional types, but it lacked popular acceptance at the time because it was not just an amplified traditional piano or could not be made to sound enough like a traditional piano. It was also much more costly than it need have been to achieve the sounds it did.

Newer efforts in a similar direction have taken similar tone sources but in simpler form and processed them electronically to produce a whole variety of new sounds. For example, a controlled amplifier using the same basic circuitry originally presaged by compressors and expanders can take the sound from plucked strings, such as a guitar or harpsichord, or the electrified versions (which have no acoustic amplification), and change the envelope of the sound.

Expansion produces an accentuated pizzicato effect by increasing the contrast; decay after the pluck is much more rapid without the tone modification that occurs when decay is speeded up by some form of mechanical damping.

On the other hand, compression takes out the contrast, softening the intensity of the pluck and making the decay seem abnormally long. It is surprising what this does to a "string" tone, making it sound much more like an organ or blown tone.

PROGRAMMED MUSIC

Not to be confused with music synthesis is the use of electronic techniques, particularly computers, to program various aspects of music generation. The first step in this direction was motivated by an interest in music composition. A number of highly sophisticated projects were initiated, based on the concept that certain sequences of notes and rhythm patterns fall "naturally" into musical forms; therefore, it should be possible to program a computer to perform musical composition.

This was one situation where theory and practice did not exactly match or prove out. To read or listen to the papers presented, a convincing case was made for the potential of such a procedure. To abbreviate the presentation somewhat, the notion was that by feeding in information about a large variety of note sequences and their associated rhythmic patterns, coupled with the kinds of mood they engender in the listener, the computer would first "recognize" pattern relationships too complicated for simple analysis with limited human resources.

The next step then would be to "request" the same computer to apply the large amount of "information" it had extracted from a vast amount of musical composition examined to produce new musical compositions that use the same principles. The assumption apparently was that by doing this the computer would sort of acquire the collective genius of as many composers as had been responsible for the original music investigated by the computer.

Which reminds me of the story about a biology professor who had a consuming ambition, about which he addressed his summer students one year. According to the story, the professor had a taste for abalone but was worried that the species might become extinct because, as he interpreted its biological environment, it is a rather defenseless creature. On the other hand, the good professor felt, a crocodile is much better equipped to defend itself. So his objective was to cross an abalone with a crocodile, thereby producing a creature with the delectable meat of the abalone with the powerful defenses of the crocodile. He had a name for his objective: abadile.

Work went on all summer, without the slightest trace of success, until the very last week, when these two creatures did by some miracle mate to produce an offspring. The only trouble was, it was not an abadile but a crocabalone!

And that is about what most listeners educed from listening to the "compositions" produced as a result of the computerized efforts. Presumably, it was expected that the close working relationship between the people involved in the project and the computer would develop a consuming ambition, rather like the one that fired the legendary professor, that would cause them to view whatever output the computer produced as "promising." However, listeners less biased realized that every composer's work expressed, along with all the moods and feelings that music can express, the composer's individual personality, often referred to as his genius. Such a combination serves not to summate the genius of many personalities but to reflect only the commonality, of which there is really very little. Certainly the computer turned out to be no genius!

Since then, however, computers have entered the picture in quite a different role: as aids to genius, which is an entirely different thing. Some of these are treated in Chapter 6 on synthesizers, but the real possibilities have only been scratched. The important thing to realize is that the real creative genius is still the musical composer, even though he may be provided with more "tools," which can include the use of one or more computers. The end result must still in some respect (and possibly more now than ever before) express the composer's personality.

In fact, an examination of this kind of work reaffirms this principle. For the early efforts of a composer sound "experimental," like a child who is still learning to play a musical instrument. Only after the composer really begins to get a "feel" for what he is doing, and wants to do, so that the computer and all the equipment used with it becomes, in effect, an extension of the composer's personality, just as the more traditional musical instrument does with the accomplished musician, does a true, recognizable personality begin to emerge. That, approximately, is where we are "at" as this book is being written: extremely promising things are coming forth in which the various composers active in such media are beginning to exhibit a true "feel" for them. For this reason, the future for electronic music now looks very promising.

Chapter 2

Amplification of Traditional Instruments

The simplest form of electronics in music is the use of amplification merely to make traditional forms of musical instruments louder or more readily heard. Tone generation and modification are attained in the traditional, nonelectronic pattern with little change. The problem with this objective is that of picking up a sound or a waveform that represents the true sound and then amplifying it so as to preserve the traditional effect, virtually unchanged.

ACCORDIANS AND CHORD ORGANS

The sound source in both these instruments is a resonant reed, energized by air flowing past it. In an accordian the space between the reeds and the grill through which the sound emanates in the traditional instrument is quite restricted (Fig. 2-1) for good reason: if a larger space were provided, the sound would be adversely affected: a cavity, or boxy sound would result.

But becuase the space where the reeds are located has this long thin shape, with the reeds distributed along it, one microphone cannot possibly pick up sound from all the reeds equally. The ideal might be a special type of microphone that extends the whole length of the reed bank, but a compromise for which most accordian amplifiers settle is that of using from three to five microphones along the length. They are spaced so the pickup from all the reeds is as near uniform as possible. A reed near one microphone will be picked up predominantly by that microphone (Fig. 2-2). A reed midway between two microphones will be picked up equally by both microphones, so that adding the electrical outputs of both microphones will result in about the same sound level as from the one close to only one microphone. In other words, the combining output of all microphones represents nearly equal pickup from all reeds.

Because at such positions it is important that the electrical outputs add, the correct phasing of the microphones is vital to success. If one microphone should be incorrectly phased, a reed equidistant from that microphone and its neighbor would inject equal sound into each mike, but the electrical outputs would be in opposition, so very little electrical output would result.

Electrical phasing can usually be achieved by consistent connection: if the microphones are parallel connected (which is common) all output leads of the same color are connected together. Only if the microphones happen to be assembled differently will the phasing be incorrect then. Ceramic microphones are invariably connected in parallel.

If dynamic microphones are used, they may be connected in series to arrive at a more convenient impedance for connecting into the amplifier (Fig. 2-3). In this case, assuming identical assembly, leads of opposite colors are connected together down the line and leads of opposite colors from the end mikes are used for the output connections.

Phasing can be checked by playing the accordian. Incorrect phasing will immediately be apparent by one or more

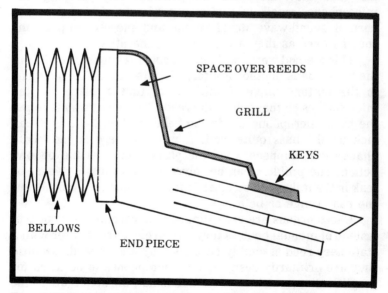

Fig. 2-1. Cross-section of an accordian keyboard showing the relatively small space between the reeds and the grill.

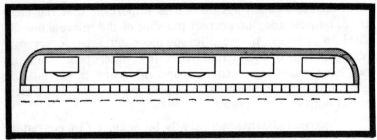

Fig. 2-2. Placement of microphones (typical) along the grill, over the reeds, to pick up the sounds from the solo end of an accordian.

very weak spots on the scale. If a microphone is not connected or not working, reeds close to it will be weaker than the rest of the scale but still quite audible. But if the connections to one microphone are reversed, notes between that mike and adjoining mikes will almost disappear, particularly at one or more certain notes, as a rule.

Microphones used for accordian pickup should be of a pressure type (not cardioid or bidirectional) and as small as possible. This is why ceramics are often preferred (along with the fact that they are inexpensive). By keeping the microphones small, they offer a minimum of obstruction to normal sound-wave development and merely amplify the sound waves as they are normally generated.

This method works well for the solo (keyboard) reeds, but the bass side is another matter. The mechanical connections to the buttons make it difficult to find a place for the microphones on that side of the reeds. The usual way is to put the bass microphone inside the bellows (Fig. 2-4), so it can pick up the bass quite well. A problem here is the "DC" change that happens when the player reverses the bellows action. The problem can be solved by an acoustic release or leak in the mike with an electrical low-frequency cutoff below the bass range or both.

Chord organs are very similar to accordians, except that instead of manual bellows they use an electrical blower with a stationary reed assembly controlled by a keyboard. Because they are primarily designed for microphones to be fitted for amplification, which an accordian is not, the space where the microphones are housed is usually better adapted for the purpose.

22

AMPLIFIED STRINGS

In this group are violins of various sizes down to the double bass, traditional guitars, and the piano (again traditional). The most common applications are with the bass violin (or double bass, as it is often called) and the guitar. The violin and piano have been electronically amplified experimentally, with some success, but such efforts have never been too successful commercially.

The inherent difference between the violin and the guitar, for this purpose, is that the violin uses gut or synthetic strings, while the guitar (to which amplification is applied, at least) uses steel strings. Of course, there are other musical differences between the instruments.

In the violin the vibrating string communicates its vibrations to the belly of the instrument by the bridge (Fig. 2-5). The belly vibrations produce air pressure waves inside the body of the instrument which radiate through the f-holes. And the vibrating shell radiates some sound as well.

As you can see in Fig. 2-5 there are three places where sound waves could be picked up: (1) where the sound waves are transmitted from the bridge to the belly; (2) inside the body of the instrument; (3) where the sound waves emerge

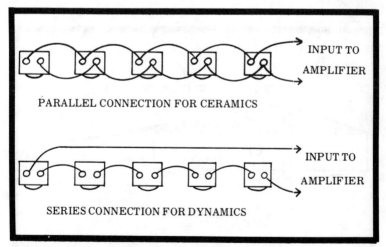

Fig. 2-3. Parallel or series microphone wiring method for correct phasing (assuming identical assembly of individual microphones).

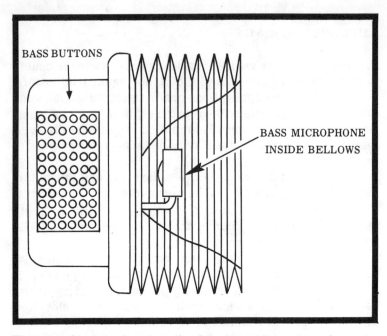

Fig. 2-4. Sketch showing the location of a microphone in-side the bellows of an accordion. In this position the bass pickup is better.

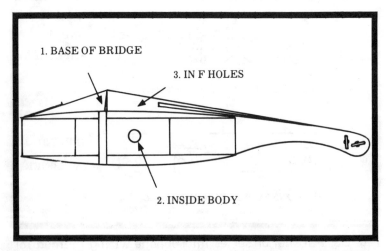

Fig. 2-5. Drawing showing three theoretical possibilities for picking up sound from a violin.

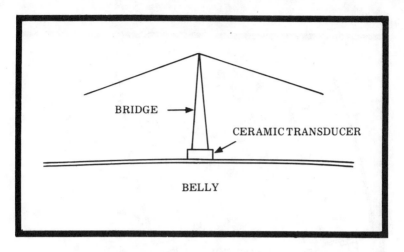

Fig. 2-6. A strain-gauge type transducer may be placed under the bridge feet on a violin to pick up pressures transmitted from bridge to the belly of the instrument.

from the f-holes. Each requires a different transducer technique. If the base of the bridge is used, a strain-gauge type transducer mounted between the bridge and the belly will transform the pressure fluctuations into electrical output (Fig. 2-6). A simple ceramic strain gauge is ideal for this.

If interior vibrations are picked up a regular pressure microphone of any type will serve. This method is not particularly convenient for small violins, but has been used successfully for bass and cello because they have a natural means of access through the floor rest (Fig. 2-7). A special floor rest (patented by Ampeg) is available; it has an extension inside to carry the microphone.

Smaller violin sounds have been amplified by a double microphone technique: one microphone picks up the sound from inside the belly, the other picks up the "stringy" effects, such as the effect of the bow, or plucking (according to how it is played), directly from the strings (Fig. 2-8).

Picking up sound at the f-holes would require a velocity or bidirectional type microphone, an approach that has never proved too successful because of the inherent fragility of such mikes and because the f-holes themselves are so delicately shaped that it is virtually impossible to "mike" the air flow through them without spoiling it.

25

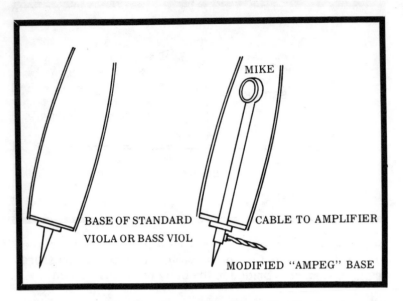

Fig. 2-7. Adaptation of bass or cello violins is simpler: the peg (left) used to support the instrument on the floor is replaced by a modified one (right) that provides mounting and lead-out for an internal microphone.

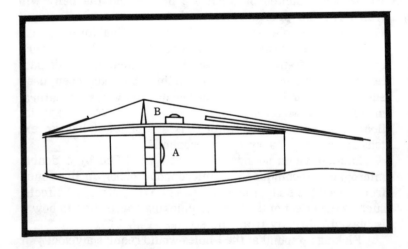

Fig. 2-8. This drawing shows mike locations used to pick up the sounds of a violin: A, microphone inside instrument, strapped to sound post; B, microphone under the strings, near the normal bowing position, to pick up bowing sounds; it is cemented to belly.

With guitars an altogether different approach is used. Because guitar strings are made of steel, magnetic pickups are generally used instead of microphones, which considerably eases the problem. Of course, any instrument of the guitar type using gut or other nonmetallic strings cannot accommodate such pickups. Now the only problem is where to place a guitar pickup.

In most cases, two sets of pickups are located under the strings, one closer to the bridge than the other. Each string vibrates at a whole variety of frequencies, harmonically related. The fundamental is the simplest form of vibration (Fig. 2-9). Harmonics are other vibrations, with one or more nodes along with the length of the string. They are related to the fundamental by being almost exactly integral multiples (2, 3, 4, etc.) of the fundamental.

The tonal quality of a string is largely determined by the musical harmonic structure: the relative magnitudes of vibration at the fundamental and the sequence of harmonic frequencies. An important component of the overall musical quality is the initial transient, when the string is played by plucking.

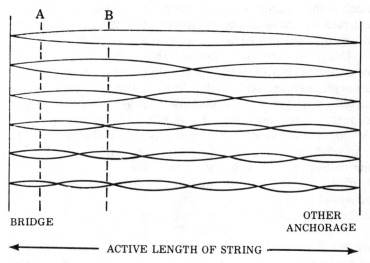

Fig. 2-9. The wavy lines depict the modes of vibration in a taut string, from fundamental (top) through various higher order harmonics or overtones. Dashed lines A and B represent the positions of the pickups used on guitars.

The continuing steady tone is a relatively steady vibratory pattern that slowly dies away and is determined by the length, weight, and tension of the string. The initial transient is not entirely determined by the same properties. A wave travels back and forth along the string, until it settles into a regular motion as a whole, determined by these properties. The initial wave motion is governed by the tension and length as well as the weight of the string, the same characteristics that determine the steady tone. But the molecular structure of the string is more dominant, which affects the simple harmonic motion at various frequencies. This behavior of the string is what produces the "twangy" effect characteristic of its being plucked.

Pickups placed fairly well away from the bridge tend to emphasize the fundamental frequency, since the fundamental represents the greatest amplitude of string movement. The other effects possess a relatively high intensity with less movement, so they produce pressures that are transferred to the bridge and thus to the body (in the traditional, nonamplified guitar).

At points close to the bridge, the strings do not move very much at the fundamental frequency. So a pickup placed there will pick up more of the overtones (harmonics) and pluck sounds than one placed further away from the bridge.

Using two pickups makes possible a wider variety of effects than is possible with the simple traditional instrument, although they are still related to it. If the pickups are connected in phase so the outputs add at the fundamental frequency, the sound will be a mixture of the tone qualities picked up at each location individually. But if the pickups are connected antiphase, the fundamentals will cancel, or be diminished; as a result the pluck tones and overtones will dominate, giving an exaggerated pizzicato effect. Most guitars of this type provide separate controls on each pickup, so the effect can be adjusted to the player's choice (Fig. 2-10).

A few successfully amplified traditional type pianos exist around the world, but they were never commercially successful. Two structural approaches are possible. The simplest method is to merely add some form of pickup or microphone to a traditional piano. The disadvantage of this approach is that it is difficult for the player, and often for anyone else, to tell exactly what the amplification does, because the piano sound

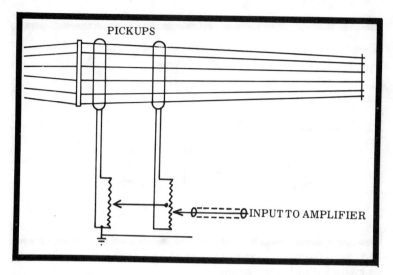

PICKUPS

INPUT TO AMPLIFIER

Fig. 2-10. The electrical connections to some guitar pickups include a provision for reversing the phase of the one remote from the bridge.

board produces a good hearty sound output without any help from the amplification.

The other method is to eliminate natural amplification in the piano by building it without a sound board so it produces very little sound without electronic or external amplification. Beyond this distinction, the choices for picking up string sounds are the same, as for other stringed instruments. A common practice, that of putting a microphone close to the sound board of the piano, hardly qualifies for consideration in a book with this title; it is no more than conventional amplification.

Picking up the sound from piano strings directly always resulted in sound that was difficult to adjust so it duplicated conventional piano sound. All kinds of variations in the sound, some of them quite fantastic, proved possible, except finding one that really sounded credibly like an ordinary piano! This is probably why the amplified piano never achieved commercial status.

Piano pickups may be either electric or magnetic, and more than one set may be used, just as in the guitar. The overall comments on tone quality very much follow those made relative to the guitar.

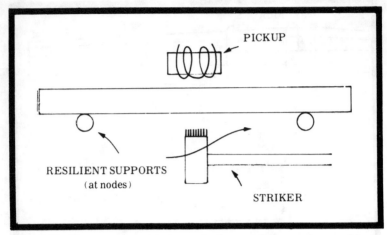

Fig. 2-11. General arrangement of one of the rods used in a so-called electronic piano.

THE ELECTRONIC PIANO

Strictly, this is not a piano at all, in the accepted sense, because it does not use strings. But it produces a musical effect not too unlike a piano, and its sound can be quieted or amplified, as desired, and thus is very convenient as a teaching or learning instrument.

The electronic piano uses rods that are struck, very much like those used as chimes in smaller household clocks. The main distinction is that instead of being mounted so the vibration is transmitted to a sound board acoustically they are mounted so there is little direct sound radiation; an electrical pickup (or less frequently a microphone) is used to allow the sounds to be amplified (Fig. 2-11).

WIND INSTRUMENTS

Some wind instruments have rather soft voices, particularly the woodwinds. Muted brass can be quite soft, too. The most common way to amplify the sound of brass is to use ordinary microphones to pick up the entire orchestral sound. This is probably the best solution for more than 90 percent of the occasions it may be needed.

However, there is one reason for using individual instrumental amplification where each is picked up directly, rather than at a distance. When acoustical problems are encountered in the hall or auditorium in which a performance is held, the only alternative is to use a microphone for each instrument. Using various pickups that develop sound almost exclusive of the acoustic sound generated by the instrument to which they are attached enables reverberation to be virtually ignored in the amplification. It is equivalent to having the instruments play louder, rather than amplifying the sound after it has been "let go" into the room or auditorium.

For wind instruments a microphone should be small so as not to obtrude into the sound-wave development; it is normally mounted on the bell, as an extension to it. Where a mute is used, the microphone must not interfere with the use of the mute (players often manipulate the mute to get special effects). And it must be mounted where the sound it picks up is representative of the sound waves radiated from the instrument. Difficulty in achieving this has been mainly responsible for very limited acceptance of individual amplification for wind instruments.

MICROPHONES AND PICKUPS

From the technician's viewpoint an important distinction exists between a microphone and a pickup. Few musicians are aware of the distinction and will often use the terms interchangeably and, therefore, often incorrectly.

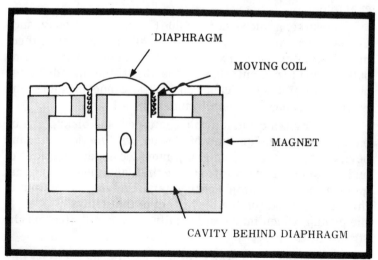

Fig. 2-12. Structural view of a dynamic type pressure microphone.

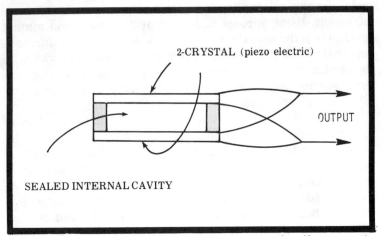

Fig. 2-13. Structural view of a sound-cell ceramic microphone.

A microphone is a device that picks up sound waves in air, whether inside or outside the instrument. A pickup is a device that picks up the vibrations that ultimately make the sound waves. Where a pickup can be used, it has advantages over a microphone in that it does not pick up extraneous sounds. A microphone can always pick up unwanted conversation, for example.

Of course, a microphone inside an instrument body, such as the bass violin or cello, picks up the sound waves there much more intensely than it would a conversation going on outside the instrument; thus, it has almost the full advantage of a pickup. Magnetic pickups on a guitar cannot pick up sound waves extraneous to the instrument at all.

Both devices come in two basic types: the pickup can be either a strain-gauge type of device or a motion-detecting device. The ceramic strain-gauge mounted under the bridge of an instrument is an example of the first, and the conventional guitar pickup an example of the magnetic type. The output of the latter depends on the movement of the strings relative to the pickup, which imposes virtually no loading effect on the strings in the process.

Microphones generally are pressure or velocity instruments. The pressure type responds to variations in air pressure due to the sound waves. An essential feature is that it

32

have a diaphragm of some sort, only one side of which is exposed to the sound waves. Usually this is coupled to the transducer in some way (Fig. 2-12). One successful and quite small microphone uses tiny ceramic crystals back to back, with an enclosed space between them, so that the crystals themselves constitute both the diaphragm and the transducer (Fig. 2-13). This is commonly called a "sound-cell" ceramic.

Whatever the details of its structure, a pressure microphone must have a contained air space. The diaphragm is moved by the sound-wave pressure variations, as they compress and rarify the enclosed air, to match the compressions and rarefractions of the air outside the microphone.

Any pressure microphone should have a pressure release, in the form of a small hole or tube, that allows the inside air pressure to equalize to the static air pressure outside. This serves a function similar to that of the eustachian tube in the human ear (the one that makes your ears 'pop' when you change altitude and thus air pressure).

With a velocity microphone both sides of its diaphragm are accessible to passing sound waves (Fig. 2-14). Thus the diaphragm and the transducer element, of whatever kind, moves with the air particles that transmit the sound wave, rather than responding to variations in air pressure due to the wave.

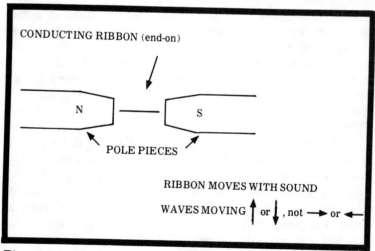

Fig. 2-14. Horizontal cross-section (looking down vertically) of a ribbon microphone, which is typical of the bidirectional type.

The significance of this distinction can best be appreciated by considering how an air cavity resonates to a particular note (Fig. 2-15). Inside the cavity the air moves very little but its pressure changes as air moves in and out of the neck of the cavity. In the neck of the cavity there is very little change in the actual pressure, but the air moves in and out rapidly to accomplish the exaggerated (due to resonance) changes of pressure inside.

Thus, a pressure microphone inside the cavity, or a velocity microphone in its neck, could be used to pick up sound waves developed in the cavity. Understanding this principle is important to considering how any instrument will work best or is supposed to work at all.

Before turning from this most general distinction between microphone types to factors involved in deciding upon a suitable microphone, we should discuss other ways in which microphones differ from one another. Often, for example, a manufacturer has two or more microphone types that look substantially identical but which carry a different type number and radically different price tags.

Many have thought that because structurally the microphones appeared identical, this is the manufacturer's way of making a little extra money: selling the same microphone in quantity at a lower price for the non-professional market and at the same time putting on a different type number and upping the price for the professional market. Any manufacturer who tried that trick would not serve the professional market for very long. The fact is that, although two types are structurally the same and may in fact share the same production line for part of their manufacture, there is an important difference commensurate with the difference in price tag.

A high-quality microphone, with really smooth frequency response, involves a lot more quality control in its production than one that may still possess good quality by virtue of using the same basically good design but in which the quality control is absent. And the kind of quality control involved here is costly. The important differences are not readily visible to the eye, but they show up on critical tests.

The quality control used to produce the higher-priced mike may be no more than critical selection from a production run, with those that do not quite make the grade going in the less expensive bin. Even at that, the price differential is justifiable because you could not rework a lower-price sample to produce the higher-price product without expending more than the price differential. However, most manufacturers do more than merely select good samples. The higher-priced product gets more attention at various points on the production line to ensure not only that it is a better performing product but also that it remains that way; that it is reliable.

In a high-quality microphone the diaphragm weight is critical. More attention is given to the perfection of diaphragm balance, along with closer care to securing the voice coil and control elements. All these improvements must go together into one microphone to achieve the overall better performance. It is not sufficient to pick the better performing samples from a large quantity production, from which the rejects are sold for a much lower price. So you get what you pay for from any reputable microphone manufacturer.

But why are these fastidious details so important? Because, for almost any application, although some make it more important than others, smoothness of response makes the difference between a good microphone and a poor one. If the microphone happens to be deficient in bass, treble, or middle response in a general way, the condition can be corrected by suitable tone controls. But this kind of difference

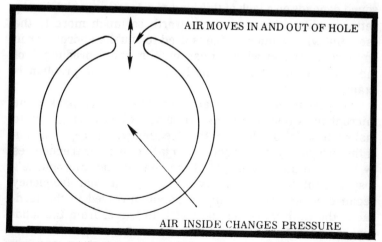

Fig. 2-15. A cavity, as a means of demonstrating the difference between pressure and velocity, as related to a resonator.

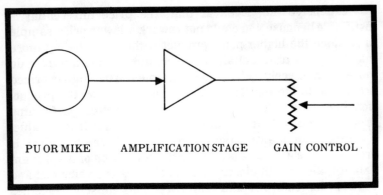

PU OR MIKE   AMPLIFICATION STAGE   GAIN CONTROL

Fig. 2-16. Some amplifiers may not work with musical instruments because the gain control fails to control distortion in the first stage.

between microphones is more one of basic design, not the fastidious details we are discussing. The little details that make differences affect smoothness of response in rather intricate ways: a little peak here or a dip there. This kind of thing costs as much or more to correct electrically as it would to buy the better microphone in the first place, and even when corrected the "doctored" microphone is not as good.

Little peaks and dips in the response lend coloration to the sound the microphone picks up. Realism in reproduction of sound depends on a lack of this kind of coloration, which is why better quality microphones are worth so much more to the user. But when a microphone is used for public address, or in any circumstances where it can pick up the reproduction of the sound it picked up originally (feedback) the problem is exaggerated by this fact.

Suppose the system is operated so that a small peak in the microphone's response lacks only 2 or 3 db of having gain to make it howl, or oscillate, at that frequency. The reproduction of this frequency is exaggerated relative to other frequencies by far more than the height of the peak in the microphone's response; it has a tendency to "ring" at that frequency because of the acoustic time constant involved in the feedback: the time taken for the sound to travel from the loudspeaker back to the microphone.

Even to restore the microphone to a point where the peak will not be emphasized more than its natural extent requires operating the system some 10 db below howl point, which often

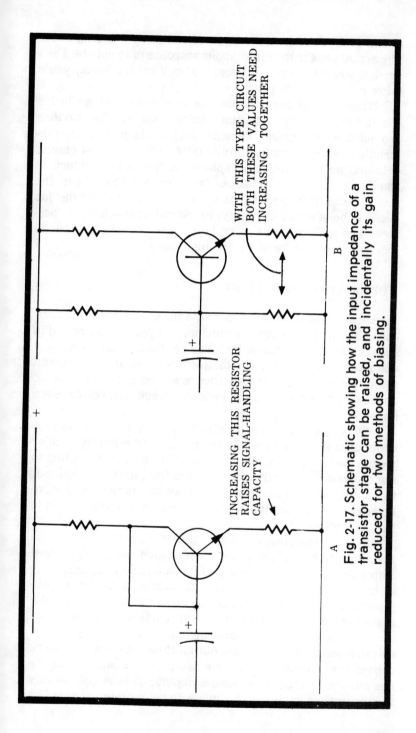

WITH THIS TYPE CIRCUIT BOTH THESE VALUES NEED INCREASING TOGETHER

B

INCREASING THIS RESISTOR RAISES SIGNAL-HANDLING CAPACITY

A

Fig. 2-17. Schematic showing how the input impedance of a transistor stage can be raised, and incidentally its gain reduced, for two methods of biasing.

means the system gives the impression it is not working at all. The actual peak in the microphone response may only be 3 or 4 db, but when the system accentuates it by feedback, you'd think it was a 20 db peak.

When microphones are used as instrument pickups inside the instrument, the situation differs again. The cavities around the microphone become part of its pickup characteristic, making it perform quite differently from test results obtained on the same microphone in free space, which is usually an anechoic chamber with no obstacles near the microphone. This means that a microphone good for the job needs to be selected carefully, based not so much on its performance specifications as on how it performs in the special location provided for it by the instrument.

APPLICATION PROBLEMS

Musical people often write to me for advice about matters connected with "miking" or "pickup." If you are interested in such matters (as you must be if you're reading this book) they will likely ask you, too. The distinction between pressure and velocity and how these quantities are used is the most basic acoustic principle to keep in mind when answering such questions.

There are electrical or electronic problems as well. A common mistake is made by simply finding a microphone or pickup that may or may not be suited for the job, according to the discussion under the previous heading, then connecting it to an amplifier which it may or may not match. You have three chances out of four of being wrong, unless you happen to be "in the know."

In this connection the word "match" has two parts to its meaning. In high fidelity work impedance matching is most important. A microphone or pickup should be connected only to an amplifier input designed to accept a device of appropriate impedance: low, line, or high. But for this work the matter of level needs attention in addition to impedance.

Because microphones and pickups appropriately placed on instruments develop more output than they would in more conventional sound work, the amplifier inputs must be designed to accept these higher inputs. This is not merely another way of saying such signals do not need much gain. An amplifier designed for low-level input often provides the gain control only after providing the first stage of amplification (Fig. 2-16). The normal reason for doing this is to improve signal-to-noise ratio or dynamic range. By raising the level before the gain control cuts it down, as may be needed, signal level is maintained that much higher above noise than if the control was placed before any amplification.

But such an input stage, intended for really low-level inputs, may easily be overloaded by a microphone or pickup on a musical instrument, and turning down the gain control does not help since the distortion has already happened. The amplifier needs either an input stage designed to receive the larger inputs that instruments can give or some attenuation ahead of the input stage.

In some instances, this can be changed by appropriate alteration or operating values on the input stage: change of bias, for example, or use of some feedback to reduce gain in a way that will allow the stage to accept a bigger input signal. In a transistor stage using a larger value emitter resistor (Fig. 2-17) will achieve this. But if the bias is of the type shown in Fig. 2-17B, the lower bias resistor as well as the emitter resistor need changing. Select a value that brings the collector voltage back to correct operating reading.

Possibly the easiest way if you don't have time to analyze the situation is to insert appropriate attenuation (Fig. 2-18). In

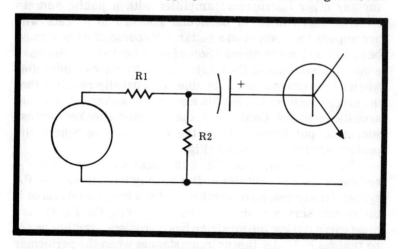

Fig. 2-18. An attenuator may be inserted at the input rather than change the internal circuitry.

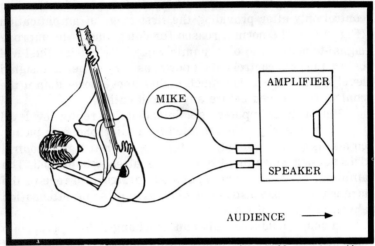

Fig. 2-19. A singer, accompanying himself on a guitar, without a PA system in the auditorium, will normally arrange his equipment somewhat like this.

this case, see that both devices are properly matched: the amplifier and the microphone or pickup, and do not forget in figuring the attenuation to include the base input impedance in parallel with R2.

An important application problem relates to using a guitar (or any other instrument) amplifier with a public address system. This can be of particular concern to singers who accompany themselves on a guitar. (Of course, the vocal must be pickup by a microphone.) Some instrument amplifiers have a microphone input so the musician can use his own amplifier when a PA system is not available. This usually requires that the singer perform behind his amplifier-speaker set to avoid acoustic feedback. Conversely, the amplifier-speaker box(es) should be put forward from the mike location where the performer sings and plays (Fig. 2-19).

The arrangement in Fig. 2-19 works well if a local PA system is ignored (not used). But he may have to use the PA system for one reason or another. If it is a big auditorium or if the system serves an overflow listening area, the PA system must carry it. Now the musician has a problem, whether or not he realizes it. Under these circumstances when the performer puts his system out front (Fig. 2-19) he finds he cannot hear himself as he is accustomed to doing. Otherwise, this is

40

probably the best arrangement, whether or not he uses his own mike in addition to the PA mike.

A method often preferred by the performer is to put his speakers to the side or behind him (Fig. 2-20). Now the PA mike picks up two sounds: the performer direct and the sound from his speakers. If he uses his own mike, his voice will carry an echo effect due to the double pickup. This may enhance or detract from the desired effect.

If the performer uses only the PA mike, the guitar still gets double treatment. This will not be so identifiably an echo effect, but may be more noticeable for its phase interference patterns. These take time to build up and can give the guitar a sound almost like the wow associated with some poor recordings.

Unfortunately many performers do not allow time to check such things thoroughly in advance. Another factor is that of contracts with the various people involved. The per-

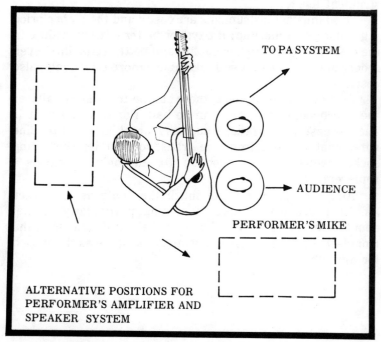

Fig. 2-20. When the house PA system must also be used, an alternative arrangement, such as one of those shown here, may be better, but there may still be problems.

former may have his own PA man to handle use of his equipment while the auditorium also has its own PA man. Sensible technical people can usually work out the best solution between them, but contracts sometimes make otherwise sensible people behave differently.

TROUBLESHOOTING

If you are a technician normally involved in this field, you will probably be called upon to service someone's instrument which has quit working or is not working to his satisfaction. The most common cause of trouble in equipment of this type concerns connecting leads, which are apt to receive much abuse and are often not of the quality usually provided for professional studio equipment. The musical instrument market is highly competitive, and many musicians do not seem to value the amplification part (at least until it fails to perform) proportionately with their appraisal of the instrument itself.

Good musical instruments are costly and the higher price tag is not just a markup: it pays for better craftsmanship. In the electronic part, higher quality and better reliability, even if only in the leads that will take abuse more effectively, also costs.

Aside from lead failure, there can be transducer failure; the microphone or pickup can go bad. For this, unless it is another case of lead failure, such as a break in one of the fine wires that connect from the transducer to its connecting socket, which you can probably fix, the only remedy is a replacement.

Amplifier problems are much the same as any other amplifier problems: there is nothing particularly special about amplifiers built for musical instruments, and troubleshooting procedures are much the same as those used for any other amplifier.

Chapter 3

Electronic Modifiers

Under the category of electronic modifiers are those instruments that still depend on the same basic tone generators used by traditional instruments through the centuries: vibrating strings, reeds, rods, the air in pipes, etc.; but electronic means are used to do more than simply amplify the traditional forms: they modify as well.

We could present this as a sort of generic development, but that would not be strictly true, although undoubtedly it has been present. All forms of electronic music are products of this 20th century, during which advances in many fields have been rapid and simultaneous. As well as new ideas growing more or less by accident out of earlier experiments with the same things, there has been some borrowing from other fields.

For example, some of the things that have been done with guitar sound modification were developed by such an "accident." The technique of placing more than one pickup under the strings very probably came about by chance. As a result we've learned to capitalize on the effects attainable by combining the outputs. Other effects have been borrowed from sounds already perfected in the electronic organ and only later applied, to whatever extent possible, to a musical instrument such as the guitar; vibrato, for example.

The predominant distinction between musical instruments discussed in this Chapter and those in Chapter 2 may be viewed this way: those in Chapter 2 are simply traditional instruments amplified; those in this Chapter are what are commonly called "electric..." guitar, bass, what-have-you. This distinction is not precisely the same as the definition we chose, but it is substantially coincident in most instances.

Based on this predominant distinction, we have two musically distinguishable classes of instrument. A traditional guitar provided with amplification still sounds substantially similar to a traditional guitar. An electric guitar, which possesses no acoustic means of amplification comparable to the traditional type but uses a rigid board as the base, lacks the character of the traditional instrument altogether and must provide whatever character it achieves by electrical or electronic means.

The same is true to an even greater degree in the distinction between the amplified traditional bass violin, using the Ampeg device described in Chapter 2, and the electric bass, which is a little larger physically than an electric guitar: these two instruments have totally different character.

Many dyed-in-the-wool musicians may yet deny that an electric bass has any character. In the traditional sense, it does not. But it does possess a character of its own. Its strings are loaded so that a shorter string length can produce the same fundamental tone as a longer string in the traditional instrument. This loading, consisting of wire spirally wound on the main tension wire, also has the effect of minimizing overtone modes of vibration.

So the electric bass has much more fundamental tone and much less overtone or harmonic than its traditional counterpart. This is what the traditional musician regards as lacking character. To him the overtone structure emphasized by the traditional instrument body, producing a singular quality of sound peculiar to the individual instrument, was character. The electric bass certainly lacks the overtone quality.

Traditional bass players, as well as their instruments, have individual character. Each has his own way of fingering the strings. Perhaps a bass player notices this more than anyone else would. But a well-seasoned traditional bass player can listen to music in which any well-known bass player is performing and name the musician. If he is particularly astute, he might also detect if he is playing someone else's instrument and whose it is!

But the electric bass has developed similar qualities in the players. For the versatility that has gradually been built into the instruments allows the player greater flexibility to demonstrate his personal playing character than any traditional bass was capable of. So it is not so much that electric instruments do not have character as that the word character has a different property relative to it.

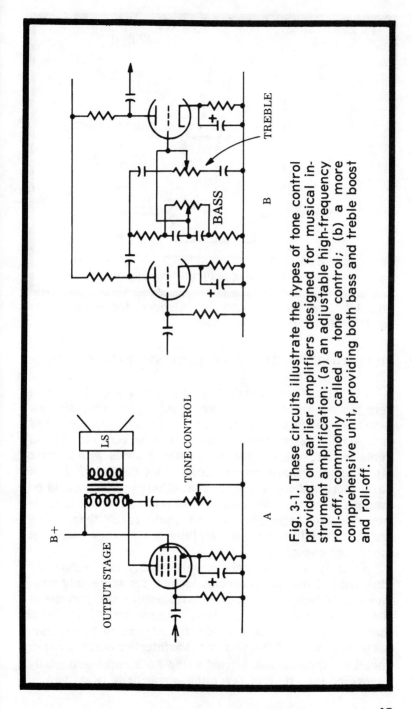

Fig. 3-1. These circuits illustrate the types of tone control provided on earlier amplifiers designed for musical instrument amplification: (a) an adjustable high-frequency roll-off, commonly called a tone control; (b) a more comprehensive unit, providing both bass and treble boost and roll-off.

45

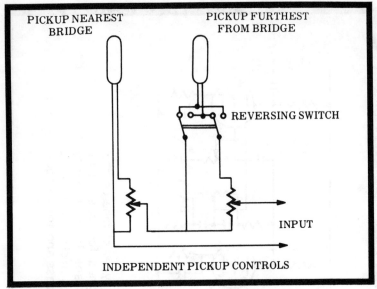

PICKUP NEAREST BRIDGE

PICKUP FURTHEST FROM BRIDGE

REVERSING SWITCH

INPUT

INDEPENDENT PICKUP CONTROLS

Fig. 3-2. One form of control intended for a guitar or electric bass with two pickups.

FROM TONE CONTROLS TO TONE SYNTHESIS

The earliest guitar amplifiers, accordion amplifiers, etc., were merely amplifiers into which microphones or pickups mounted on or in guitars or accordions were connected. And such amplifiers probably came with tone controls: just a treble roll-off, with variable resistance in series with a shunt capacitor, or a more comprehensive tone control (Fig. 3-1). Early users undoubtedly found that different effects could be obtained with these elementary controls and asked to have them mounted where the player could reach them more easily, rather than on the amplifier where they were not convenient enough for him.

As early experimenters were probably not technically educated but merely musicians looking for something new, they undoubtedly experimented with putting the pickups at different positions under the strings and found that the tonal character changed. This undoubtedly led to putting more than one pickup on the instrument, with the intention of using one **or** the other; then someone tried using both and accidentally discovered the effect of reversing connections (Fig. 3-2).

Thus the possibility of tone synthesis was discovered. If the pickups are connected so their outputs are in phase at the fundamental frequency of the string, varying the proportions of output from each pickup will provide a virtually continuous change of quality from that delivered by one pickup to that delivered by the other. But if the two outputs are connected so they combine with the fundamental out of phase, one setting of the controls will neutralize the fundamental for one note each string can play at least, while all settings will reduce the proportion of fundamental as compared with at least some of the harmonics, particularly the higher ones.

Thus some more interesting effects were born, effects which the guitar string by itself is not capable and which can be synthesized electronically. In the first instance, these effects depend on the way the strings vibrate; specifically, on the fact that they vibrate at more than one basic frequency. They also can vibrate in different directions. The direction that produces the most sound output, both in the traditional guitar and in the electrified versions, is the vibration vertically to and from the case of the instrument (Fig. 3-3).

Lateral vibration, theoretically, will produce no sound output. Actually, it may produce a frequency-doubled output (an octave higher). But the same is true relative to the

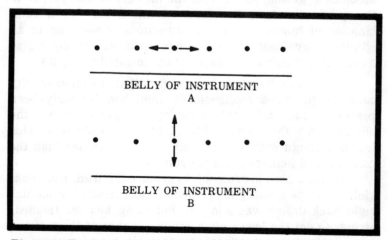

Fig. 3-3. Two basic modes of string vibration (guitar or bass strings cross section): (a) parallel with the instrument belly, giving little sound output; (b) vertical to instrument belly, giving maximum sound output.

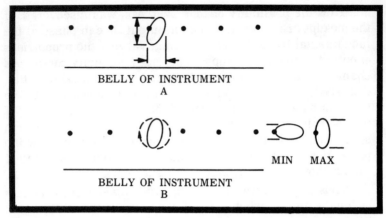

BELLY OF INSTRUMENT
A

MIN   MAX

BELLY OF INSTRUMENT
B

Fig. 3-4. More complex modes of string vibration: (a) elliptical, yielding components of the two forms shown in Fig. 3-3; (b) elliptical, with rotating axis, so the sound amplitude fluctuates or has a beat effect.

traditional guitar. The vertical vibration transmits movement through the bridge to the body of the instrument. The lateral vibration transmits a quite different form of movement with rather little acoustic sound output.

This is fortunate, in a sense, because it makes the two methods of getting sound from the instrument compatible in this particular case. Practical vibrations may be a combination of movement in both directions, amounting to an elliptical movement that may also rotate its axis slowly to give a beat effect (from a single string) as indicated in Fig. 3-4.

Once it was found that more variations in tonal quality could be produced electronically than had formerly been possible in the traditional instrument, a logical step was the elimination of the traditional features of the instrument. This led to a design with a rigid back, or body, rather than the conventional hollow-bodied instrument.

And for a bass instrument, to replace the traditional bass violin, always a bulky instrument to tote around, a similar rigid back design was adopted, but using heavier (loaded) strings to get the lower pitch range. Neither of these "electric" instruments produces appreciable sound without an amplifier, because the strings have no natural, or acoustic amplification whatever. They rely entirely on the electronic amplification to get all their effects. Electric guitars and basses have certain advantages in avoiding the problems discussed in Chapter 2, problems arising from the dual sound source; that directly from the instrument and the amplified sound from the loudspeaker. Even when an electric guitar is played close to a microphone, the microphone picks up virtually no sound from the strings, so the audible result is almost entirely dependent on the amplification.

VIBRATO & TREMOLO

The first form of purely electronic modification to be added was probably vibrato or, to be more exact, tremolo. As electronic organs have such a pleasant form if vibrato is a built-in feature, musicians naturally expected their electronic "cousins" to come across with the same thing for them.

It is not quite that easy. Most electronic organs achieve vibrato at the source of the tone by warbling the tone generator in one way or another. A quite popular form varies the tuning of the oscillator by changing the effective value of the tuning capacitor rhythmically (Fig. 3-5). For a pure electronic instrument, which we get to in Chapter 4, this kind of warbling is simple, but for an instrument that uses traditional strings as the tone source, or for an accordion, it is not easy.

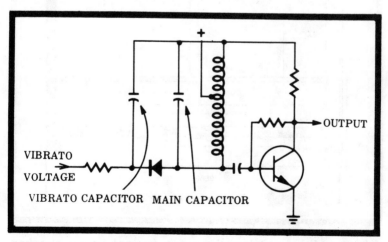

Fig. 3-5. A typical electronic organ oscillator circuit, showing how a vibrato voltage is used to warble the frequency.

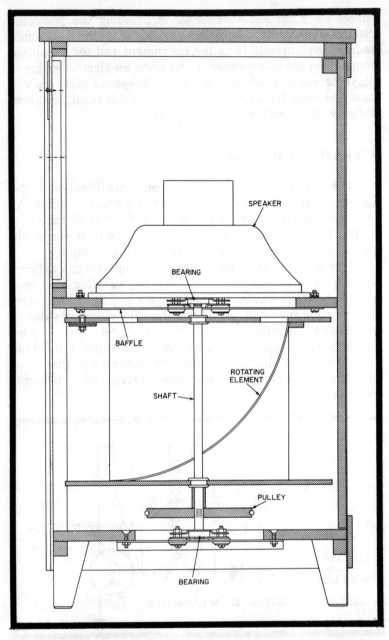

Fig. 3-6. Cross-section view of a typical Leslie speaker installation; the Leslie provides another method of achieving vibrato in electronic organs.

Tremolo and vibrato sound much the same. And to tell the truth, while some theoreticians will spend considerable time discriminating between the two, when referred to an electronic "signal" as seen on an oscilloscope before it reaches the loudspeaker and in terms of propagated waves (the kind we listen to and call sound) there is little absolute difference between the two forms.

This can be shown by a frequency analysis of the two forms. Academically, tremolo is a fluctuation of amplitude applied to a sound of constant frequency. In traditional instruments it may be achieved by opening and closing a shutter that attenuates the sound passing through it. The old home harmonium of a few generations ago did this, with the name "vox humana" (not to be confused with the true stop of that name on professional organs). Vibrato is a variation of pitch, a fluctuation of frequency, applied to a sound of constant amplitude. In traditional instruments, the best known example is the way a violinist achieves the effect by trembling his hand so his finger rolls the string at the point where it touches the finger board.

In an electronic organ, as well as introducing vibrato by changing the oscillator frequency, it can be achieved by moving the loudspeaker assembly or by using a baffle that has the same effect by changing the distance the sound wave has to travel to escape into the room. This kind of speaker is commonly called a "Leslie" after the first one of its kind to achieve the effect (Fig. 3-6).

Suppose a frequency is modulated in one or the other of these ways, electrically or electronically, at a rate of 6 Hz, which makes a good vibrato or tremolo rate. Say the frequency is a concert pitch A of 440 Hz. The pure tremolo, or fluctuating amplitude, will add frequencies of 434 and 446 Hz, in equal proportions and phased so that together they alternately add to and subtract from the steady 440 Hz waveform, without shifting the phase of the resultant wave (Fig. 3-7). So the frequency content of a concert A with tremolo is a dominant 440 Hz with smaller (and equal) amounts of 434 and 446 Hz.

Now assume the frequency is shifted at the same rate, in what is called vibrato. Frequency shift can also be interpreted as phase shift. When frequency is raised, phase advances; when frequency is lowered, phase delays. They are not the

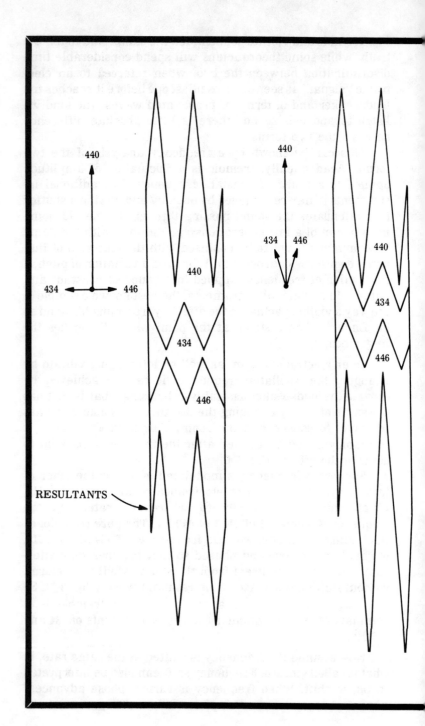

440

434 ← → 446

440

434 446

440

434

446

RESULTANTS

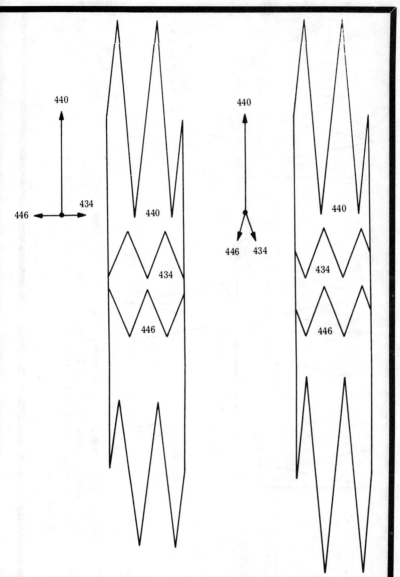

Fig. 3-7. Waveforms illustrating the phase relationships of the component frequencies, shown at one-twenty-fourth second intervals, for a 440-Hz tone with tremolo at 6 Hz. In this and Figs. 3-8, 3-9, and 3-10, waveforms are shown triangular for simplicity; actual waveforms would be sinusoidal.

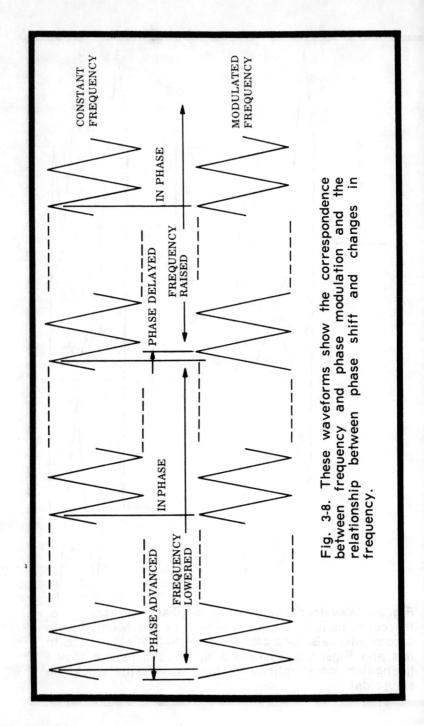

Fig. 3-8. These waveforms show the correspondence between frequency and phase modulation and the relationship between phase shift and changes in frequency.

same but are related. They can be regarded only in interchangeable terms so long as frequency is repetitively changing as happens in vibrato.

If the same frequency, 440 Hz, is alternately advanced and retarded in phase at a rate so that the complete variation is repeated six times a second, the frequency will wobble above and below 440 Hz while maintaining that average value. How far above or below 440 Hz the frequency swings will depend on how far the phase shifts from its median value in each one-twenty-fourth of a second (a guadrant of the 6-Hz variation, Fig. 3-8).

Regardless of how far the frequency shifts, the fact that its rate or repetition frequency is 6 Hz means that the phase movement repeats at that rate. Consequently, the most dominant effect in an analysis of the frequency content will be the same two frequencies produced by the tremolo but in different phase relationship (Fig. 3-9).

To keep the amplitude constant, if more than a few degrees of phase change occur other sideband frequencies such as 428 and 452 Hz will have to be added (Fig. 3-10). But the dominant ones will still be 434 and 446 Hz. And in a practical situation, a warbling tone will seldom fluctuate only its amplitude or only its frequency without affecting the other.

Even when the tone generated is produced by pure frequency or pure amplitude variation, the acoustic wave it produces has to travel round a room with real dimensions before we hear it. Thus the wave delivered to the loudspeaker may be pure tremolo, for example, but before it has left the diaphragm very far, it will have components of vibrato in it as well because of the phase shifts that occur as the various component-frequency waves travel across the room, or vice versa.

Admittedly, vibrato can give a richer sound than tremolo, for a reason that should be fairly obvious from the foregoing discussion. In generating tremolo the only extra frequencies added are a single pair of sidebands. A deep vibrato can add quite a number more frequencies. But a shallow vibrato produces essentially the same frequencies as tremolo.

Where the tone being modulated has a relatively high frequency, a vibrato will cause the phase to "go round" a few times at least, compared to a wave of the same steady frequency. This means that tremolo cannot possibly have as

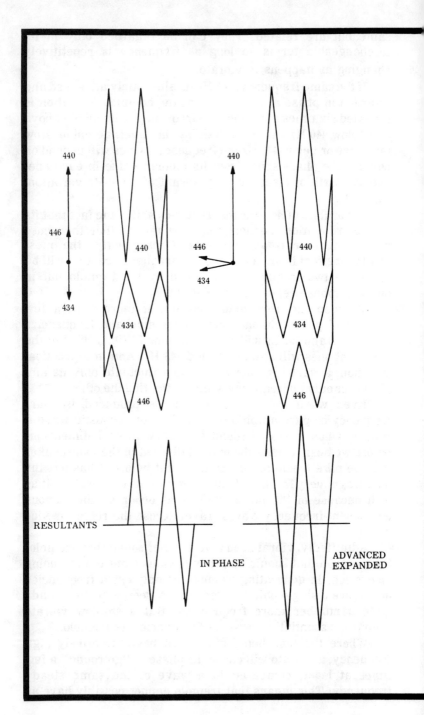

RESULTANTS

IN PHASE

ADVANCED
EXPANDED

440

446

434

56

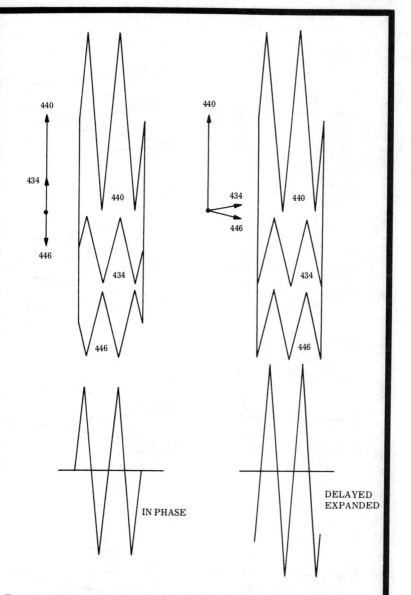

Fig. 3-9. Here we use the same frequencies but at different phase relationships from those shown in Fig. 3-7; the result is predominantly phase or frequency modulation, accompanied by a lesser degree of amplitude modulation at double the frequency (12 Hz, instead of 6Hz).

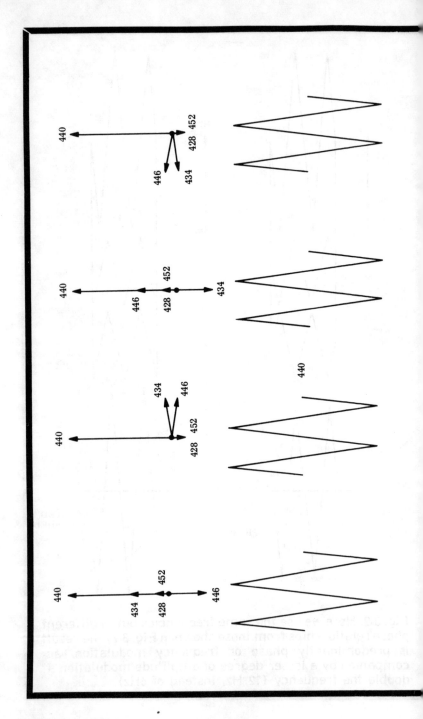

58

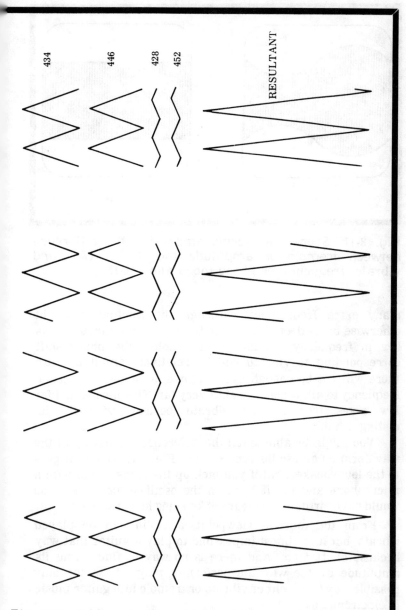

Fig. 3-10. Adding further sideband frequencies virtually eliminates the amplitude modulation from the resultant waveform in Fig. 3-9, leaving pure frequency or phase modulation (vibrato).

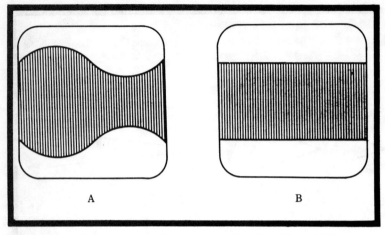

Fig. 3-11. Scope waveforms emphasize the difference between tremolo or amplitude modulation (A), and vibrato, frequency or phase modulation (B).

many extra frequencies, although the fluctuation might otherwise be as deep. But where the tone being modulated is low in frequency, as in the bass notes, the phase shift corresponding to vibrato will be relatively small because there will not be enough cycles above or below the normal frequency to allow phase to shift very far. This means that for low notes tremolo and vibrato become virtually indistinguishable.

You might be able to tell the difference by looking at the waveform on an oscilloscope screen (Fig. 3-11) before it goes to the loudspeaker, but if you pick up the same sound with a microphone and put it back on the oscilloscope screen you would have virtually no means of knowing how it started.

From the musical viewpoint, a violin can be played vibrato, but it is almost impossible to play a guitar that way because of its frets. And there is no way of fluctuating its amplitude by the way the performer plays it, so the only possible way to get either vibrato or tremolo into guitar music is electronically.

Applying tremolo is relatively easy, except for one rather severe problem. Any device that varies gain does so by changing an applied DC voltage. In tube amplifier days a vari-mu tube was used; nowadays this can be replaced by an FET

(Fig. 3-12). With either one the DC fluctuation that causes the change in gain that represents tremolo appears as a high amplitude DC signal component in the output. This gives rise to a phenomenon known as "thump" which is difficult to eliminate.

One possibility is to use two vari-mu tubes or two FETs (Fig. 3-13) in antiphase and then recombine at the output. But this invloves two phase inverters, or else a complementary symmetry pair of variable gain devices (FETs, which have not been easy to obtain with any degree of exactness so far) so that the DC is combined with the signal in opposite phase (Fig. 3-14).

To an accomplished accordionist a tremolo amplifier is little help because skillful operation of the bellows can achieve the same effect, perhaps even more, because tonal quality as well as amplitude changes when fluctuating air pressure is applied to the reeds. But a true vibrato applied to an accordion as well as to a guitar does offer something musically new. And there is a relatively easy way to achieve this, although a good one may become fairly costly (compared to some other circuits, at least).

This is achieved by applying a variable phase shift into the amplifying sequence. As a single phase shift cannot shift phase more than a total of somewhat less than 180 degrees, or

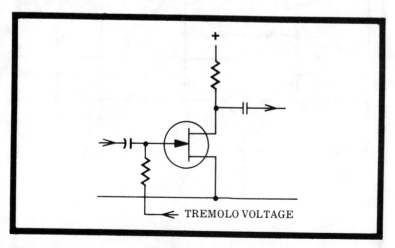

Fig. 3-12. Basic single-ended tremolo modulating stage, using an FET.

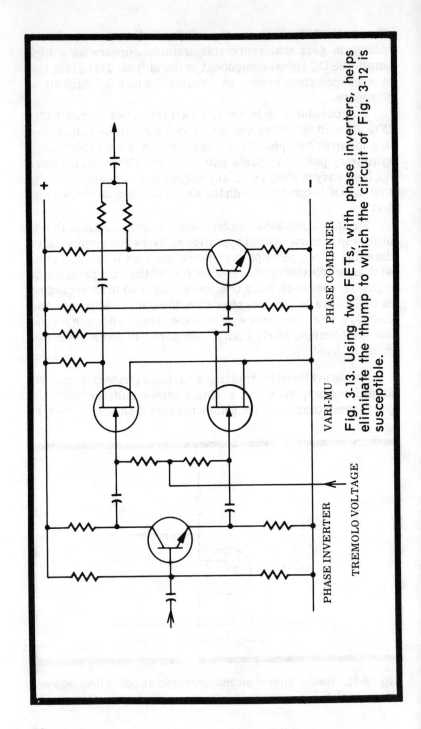

Fig. 3-13. Using two FETs, with phase inverters, helps eliminate the thump to which the circuit of Fig. 3-12 is susceptible.

PHASE COMBINER

VARI-MU

TREMOLO VOLTAGE

PHASE INVERTER

+

—

half a wave, it does not yield enough vibrato effect to be really noticeable. A good one uses the same method, applying a single vibrato supply to control several phase-shift networks, operating on the signal in succession.

The heart of these phase shifts is a variable resistance that is part of a phase-shift network. By using two variable resistances, fed by antiphase DC outputs from the vibrato oscillator (about 6 Hz) the DC injected into the signal path is neutralized (Fig. 3-15).

The variable resistance elements can be either varistors or appropriately biased diodes. This circuit introduces virtually pure vibrato because varying the resistance bridging the outputs from a phase inverter, with a capacitor as the other element, swings the output phase round a semicircle (Fig. 3-16) from the voltage at the collector to that at the emitter of the phase splitter.

Such a swing can be achieved only over a limited range of frequencies with a given capacitor and resistance variation.

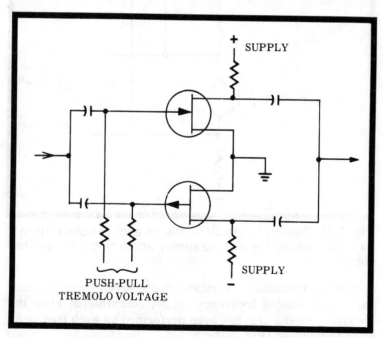

Fig. 3-14. A theoretical circuit that would achieve the same effect as the circuit in Fig. 3-13, but which would require complementary symmetry FETs, as yet not available.

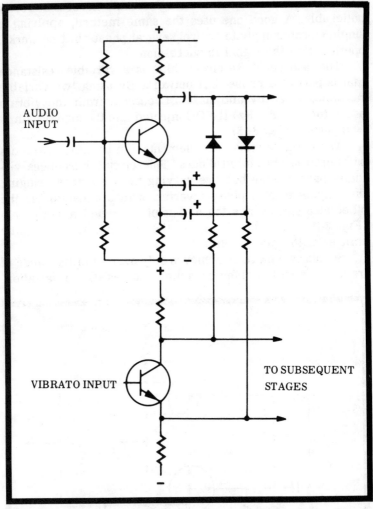

Fig. 3-15. Basic circuit elements of a phase-shift vibrato circuit, showing the vibrato supply and a single phase-shift stage.

So a more sophisticated version will use several such circuits, each for a limited frequency range, recombining after the frequency modulation has been performed on each frequency band separately (Fig. 3-17).

At one time, anything as elaborate as this would have been both prohibitively costly and quite bulky, like occupying a whole rack full of equipment. But modern solid-state

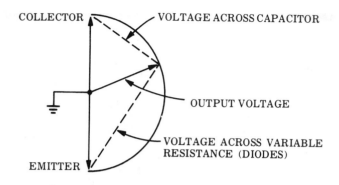

Fig. 3-16. This diagram illustrates the phase shift available from a single stage of the type shown in Fig. 3-15.

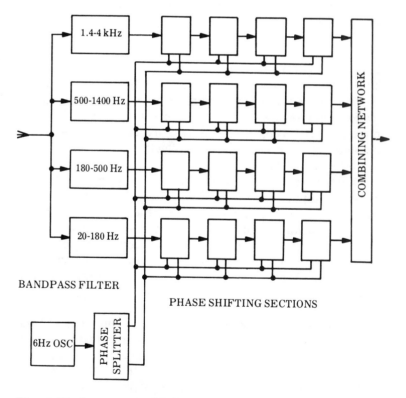

Fig. 3-17. A more sophisticated vibrato system, based on modular unit construction.

65

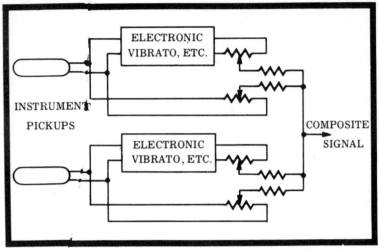

Fig. 3-18. A more composite set of controls enabling a choral effect to be obtained from a guitar or electric bass.

technology has made it possible to multiferate circuits of this kind at relatively low cost and in extremely compact form.

The above is a purely electronic effect, assuming a single audio signal as input. Even more effects are possible, if the multiple pickups on a guitar or bass are kept separate at their outputs, for different treatment electronically before being combined (Fig. 3-18).

Another of the almost infinite variety of tricks is to give constant amplification to the output from the pickup nearest the bridge of the instrument while the other is treated to a gain change utilizing a variable resistance effect that changes circuit balance. The fundamental component in the output can then reverse phase rhythmically without the conventional progressive phase change and while the bulk of the overtones change very little (Fig. 3-19). This produces a phantom-like effect in the music.

More elaborate effects are possible by using the electronic vibrato; it is possible to mix outputs with different phasing applied with unmodulated outputs which are amplified conventionally to produce choir effects, sounds that resemble many more strings being played at once. Applied to a 12-string guitar, for example, the effect can become very large, musically.

66

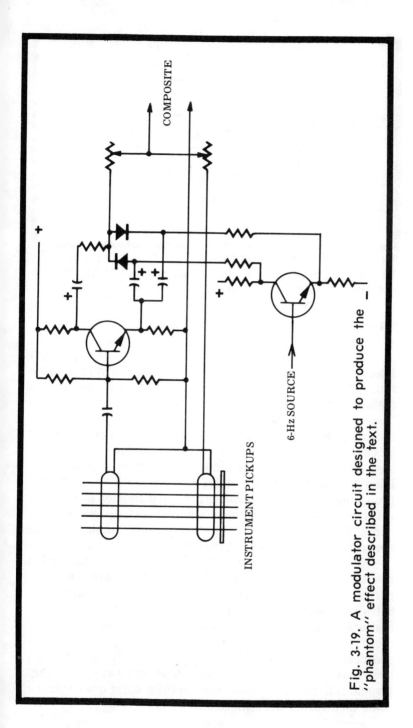

Fig. 3-19. A modulator circuit designed to produce the "phantom" effect described in the text.

67

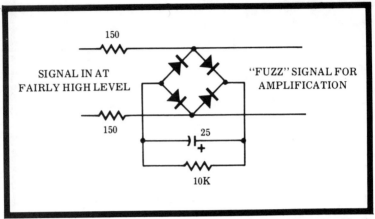

Fig. 3-20. A simple circuit that will produce a "fuzz" effect. To make the degree of "fuzz" adjustable, substitute a variable resistor for the one shown as 10K.

OTHER ELECTRONIC EFFECTS

After struggling for several decades to develop high fidelity reproduction that would bring into anyone's home musical sounds with a purity formerly found only in the highest quality instruments, some of the younger generation have recently reverted somewhat. To them music is not "loud" unless it is highly distorted. The volume control must be capable of overloading the amplifier, or the system is not loud enough, whether its output is rated in milliwatts or kilowatts! If the system gives only 10 watts good sound, producing 11 watts with about 60 percent distortion is fine! But if it gives 50 watts good sound while 80 watts produces only about 20 percent distortion, this is a "weak" amplifier to the ears of this younger group. A curious reversion, but true.

At the same time, some of the same generation have what I still prefer to call "musical ears," to appreciate musically pure sounds. Between these differing groups, discrimination between "music" and "noise" has become a very subjective matter! This is not to say that what had gone before this "loudness' craze, jazz, off-beat rhythms such as those produced by Brubeck, etc., which equally broke with traditional forms, were not music. These forms still used what I would call musical sounds; even in their worst dischords the notes themselves were musically pure.

But the group I just referred to seems to put a premium on distortion, a literally broken-up waveform. So insistent are they on getting this kind of sound that they even devise, or have made for them, what they call "fuzz boxes," stages of amplification for insertion somewhere in the earlier part of the system that introduce deliberate distortion. This occurred about the same time that recording companies accommodated the same so-called "musical" groups by recording with distortion deliberately included on the record. It seems that the need is for the music to sound "loud" even when it is played quietly!

Another way of describing some of it would be to say it resembles the sound from a loudspeaker with a loose grill cloth that rattles against the cabinet housing all the time; every note accompanied by a buzzing sound. This kind of sound can originate when an amplifier breaks down, but a broken-down amplifier is not reliable; it may quit working altogether. The need was for a consistent broken-down sound. This urge produced the fuzz-box craze.

A relatively simple way to achieve the desired effect, with an allowable variation in level as the instrument is played, is to shunt the audio signal circuit somewhere with a full-wave rectifier that charges a capacitor across which is a resistor that allows a fairly rapid discharge (Fig. 3-20). The DC that builds up across the capacitor depends on the audio level of the moment, and the charging pulses on both peaks of the audio

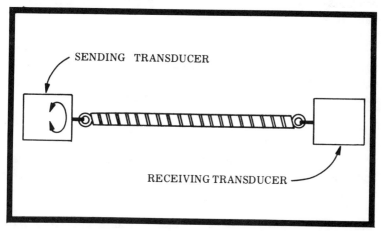

SENDING TRANSDUCER

RECEIVING TRANSDUCER

Fig. 3-21. Diagram of a mechanical type reverberation unit.

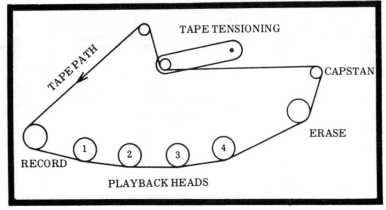

Fig. 3-22. Outline of a tape type reverberation unit.

waveform put in the desired amount of deliberate distortion. The degree of fuzz can be controlled by using a variable discharge resistor.

The fuzz-box device belongs to a category of something that performers do because it is the "in" thing. However, such diversions are a hindrance to cultural advance, in the long run, for two reasons:

(1) While many performers are engaged in exploiting temporary "insanities" like this, they are not making progress toward new sounds that may become a permanent part of a new culture.

(2) The fact that some of these diversions are undoubtedly and indisputably "unculture" leads many to disregard or reject all new things, some of which may in fact be faltering steps toward something that will eventually be worthwhile.

REVERBERATION

An addition to musical instrument design that can be acceptably musical is reverberation or echo. This can be achieved by a variety of devices, the most economical to date being the mechanical delay line: a sort of spring, set in rotational vibration by a transducer at one end. Another transducer at the other end of the spring-like device picks up the vibrations (Fig. 3-21).

70

A more sophisticated form uses a tape loop (Fig. 3-22). The program is recorded on the tape loop and picked off by playback heads along the tape path and amplified to give the desired echo effects. After the last playback head has reproduced the recorded sound, the tape is erased for reuse the next time round.

Whether one or more playback head is used, a simple means exists for changing the reverberation time: varying the tape speed. The delay depends on the time taken for sound recorded by the record head to reach the playback heads, which depends on the distance and the speed. So changing speed, changes time. As the tape passes all heads at the same speed, changing speed does not change pitch, except for the moment during a speed change.

The mechanical type delay line is subject to outside vibration. If the case in which the reverb unit is housed should be kicked, bumped, or jolted, the reverb unit will produce a characteristic "bed-spring" sound. Some performers actually like this feature, using it much like they might slap the body of their guitar for effect, except that the effect is quite different!

The tape unit is more precise in its effect. In fact, if only one playback head is used, it is almost too precise: no natural echo is quite that sharply defined. The same echo can be used repetitively, by suitable connection, but that seems to exaggerate the preciseness by the uniformity of time spacing

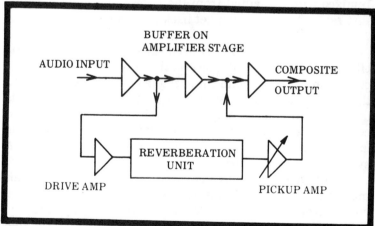

Fig. 3-23. Block diagram of a reverberation unit connected so it is inherently stable but yields only one echo or set of echoes.

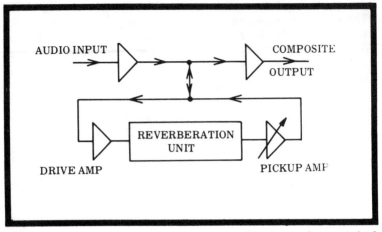

Fig. 3-24. This connection allows a continuing echo or set of echoes but must be kept within a specific gain limit to avoid instability.

between successive echoes and the unnatural evenness with which the sound decays.

This leads to a discussion of the electronic methods of connecting a reverb unit of either type. If only a single echo is required, and that perhaps at a level approaching or even exceeding that of the original sound, the direct sound must be remixed with the output from the reverb unit in such a way that reverb output cannot get back into its own input (Fig. 3-23).

This enables some really pronounced but short-term echo effects to be obtained. The alternative is to connect the reverb output back into the main channel at a point where it can feed through the reverb unit again (Fig. 3-24). When this method is used, at no frequency may the reverb's amplified output exceed the level of the same frequency at its input, or it will build up to a howl like the acoustic howl that occurs when a PA system is turned up too high.

Some what like many PA systems, the problem with this method is that unless gain is operated fairly close to this limit, not much reverb is noticeable; the effect dies away much too quickly. Using this method also necessitates care to see that the reverb unit's frequency response, overall, is as uniform as possible; otherwise, the reverb will seem to act only at certain frequencies and to be virtually dead at others.

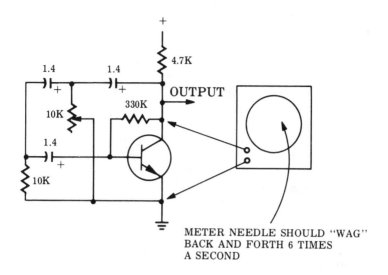

Fig. 3-25. Checks to determine whether or not a vibrato or tremolo oscillator is working.

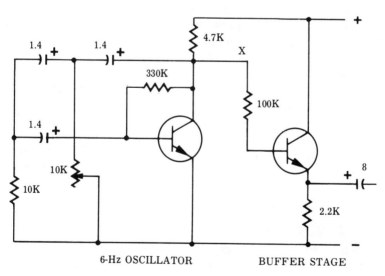

Fig. 3-26. A buffer stage is needed to prevent output loading from disabling a vibrato or tremolo oscillator. If the buffer stage is suspected of preventing oscillation, try disconnecting at Point X.

73

PUTTING A SYSTEM TOGETHER

Having covered the essential parts of a musical instrument system in this category, the musician is anxious to incorporate more or less of these variations and he wants to do so with the most control at his finger tips, or perhaps within toe's reach, using a foot control.

An instrument has only so much space for controls and the player's fingers can do only so many things at once. So a foot control is often included, particularly for on-off type functions. For example, a foot control might turn a reverb on and off, with the level of desired reverb being preset by controls on the amplifier or reverb unit. Or a vibrato can be controlled, in and out, by a foot control.

Connections to do all these things must be properly made. Controls on the instrument itself usually are volume, tone, and any other variations effected at the input before any amplification occurs. Foot controls can be used as remotes for main controls normally on the amplifier or its associated assembly.

Another question many musicians want answered is how they can get this or that new feature into their system. For example, they do not have reverb, or vibrato, or fuzz, or whatever it is, and they want to include it somehow, without buying a whole new system. If the amplifier system came with the instrument and makes no provision for such additions of any kind, it will probably cost more than it is worth to make the addition; better to get a system that provides for such extras to be inserted, using the one he has as a trade-in.

Most of the extras need to be inserted at the "front end," between the instrument and the main or power amplifier. They may be inserted in different inputs, so compound effects can be obtained; some outputs with the added effect, some without it. And possibly they can be cascaded, one after another.

The important thing is that both level and impedance match at the input and output of everything in the system. A practical feature is that connections shall match physically. But neither one (electrical or physical) being right ensures the other. If impedance and level are correct but connectors do not mate, it is usually possible to change connectors so they do. But if the connectors mate without impedance and level being right, some extra electronic circuitry is needed to achieve the match.

TROUBLESHOOTING

For this category of instrument, you need a little more background in the special devices discussed in this Chapter, devices that are not usually applied with traditional instruments that use only amplifiers. Sometimes pickups become faulty. They need replacing with the exact same type to have the same pickup characteristics as well as the same output impedance and method of mounting.

If you are called to service a vibrato or tremolo, do not assume from its name that it does precisely what the name implies. As we pointed out, a true tremolo fluctuates amplitude while a vibrato fluctuates frequency or phase (actually both, but functionally it's one or the other). But some units called vibrato really work on amplitude. The other misnomer is less frequent because circuits to vary phase are rarer and usually called by their correct name.

If such a unit fails to function, the first thing to know is how it is supposed to function. Obviously, any electronic vibrato or tremolo must have a low-frequency oscillator, working somewhere around 6 Hz. It is not difficult to find out whether this is working. Applying a DC voltmeter to the output from the oscillator, where it feeds the modulating stage, will show whether the signal is present; the meter needle should "wag" at the oscillator frequency (Fig. 3-25).

If the oscillator is not working, the first step is to fault-trace it. An oscillator is unlike an amplifier in that it either works, in which case there is an output, or doesn't, in which case there is not. An amplifier may work so far, in which case you trace signal as far as it goes. But if an oscillator does not work, there is no signal to trace.

This makes fault-tracing an oscillator a little more difficult than an amplifier. First step is to check operating voltages and deduce that associated circuits are in order. Then check the coupling circuits by continuity testing, pulse-testing the capacitors, and so forth. If operating conditions are correct, the active device (tube or transistor) checks out OK, and coupling circuits are all OK, the oscillator should work.

One more thing can prevent it: output loading. Unless a buffer stage is provided to prevent output loading (Fig. 3-26), any excessive load (lower impedance than it should be) may prevent the oscillator from functioning. Disconnect the oscillator from the circuit it modulates. If it now oscillates, the trouble is due to loading by the other circuit, which needs fault-tracing, assuming it was known to work before.

If the oscillator is working, but no vibrato or tremolo appears, something may be wrong with the modulator stage or with the coupling from the oscillator to the modulator stage. Every modulator stage uses some active device: a vari-mu tube, FET, diodes, varistors, to name a few. If the active device quits, for some reason, the signal may still transmit but it will not have vibrato or tremolo.

Another trouble often encountered in tremolo or vibrato circuits is thumping: an audio output (often loud enough to make the speaker bang) at the oscillator frequency, like a pulsing DC. Every circuit must have some design precaution to prevent this. We covered some methods earlier in this Chapter. If in one element of a pair, which was designed so the combined effect would neutralize thump, fails, then the thump will show up badly. If two vari-mu devices are used and one of them fails, signal will still get through, almost undiminished, and there still will be vibrato, but there will also be thump with a vengeance.

Sometimes thump will appear but not badly enough to be sure whether anything is really wrong. Of course, there should not be any thump in a good system. In this case it may be due to a lack of balance in neutralizing the thump. This could be due either to poor adjustment or to one component becoming partially defective. It could also be due to poor matching between a pair of components that are supposed to be a matched pair, such as diodes or varistors.

In a multistage vibrato, or in one that provides vibrato separately for different portions of the audio spectrum, a defect in one stage or in one channel could result in either thumping, a reduction in the degree of vibrato, or vibrato that is better at some frequencies than others.

A fuzz unit that fails to fuzz is a rarity, so comment on that is unnecessary. Amplifiers sometimes fuzz for free, when they are not supposed to do so, and than can prove much more of a headache.

Reverberation is fairly straightforward. It involves amplifiers and transducers that can be fault-traced quite normally. And if anything goes wrong with the delay line, whether of the mechanical (spring) or magnetic (tape) type, the fault is obvious enough not to need instructions spelling out how to find it. A broken spring or tape is easy to see, and needs replacing with the requisite duplication. Don't try a makeshift substitute, except as a very last and very temporary resort; it could ruin your reputation!

Chapter 4

Fully Electronic Instruments

The realm we begin to enter in this Chapter is fascinating indeed: it is really the wild blue yonder of electronics! It is rapidly coming of age; it is becoming something meaningful, of real musical, cultural and entertainment value. And to do this, it has come a long way, indeed.

You could say that the violin came a long way from the first string stretched over some primitive "bridge" on a flat board. But all that happened so long ago that mankind has forgotten it. Names like Maggini or Stradivari became legend for their work, being craftsmen who kept the secrets of their quality in the family and who never employed PR men to tout their merits or write their advertising copy! Good violin makers have emulated their products for centuries since. But today's generation knows little of all that.

Every traditional instrument, as we know it, needed perfecting to reach the high musical tone quality for which it eventually became known. This was a labor of love, technologically somewhat in the dark; they experimented until they found a musical quality that was acceptable and generally described as "rich." They found it had to do with shape, construction, critical dimensioning, surfacing finish, and so forth.

The electronic musical instrument designer was faced with a similar problem and a completely different set of starting facts. Even when he had made this new thing that was capable of producing some musical sound of whatever kind, traditional or new, he then had to learn to play it before he could even demonstrate it! For these new instruments were not electronic violins or a revision of some other traditional form.

HISTORICAL DEVELOPMENT

The earliest truly electronic musical instrument was the Theremin, named after its inventor. What he really did was to slightly refine an old regenerative radio receiver. To increase the gain of those early receivers (which used rather inefficient triode tubes because nothing better had yet been invented, a reaction coil was added to each tuned circuit usually with the major tuned circuit in the grid and the reaction coil connected to the plate (Fig. 4-1).

Critical adjustment of the reaction "condenser" (as a capacitor was called in those days) would make the circuit oscillate and, if the tuning was slightly off the frequency of the incoming signal, a heterodyne whistle resulted. Careful tuning could bring the circuit in tune, to the zero-beat condition, so the oscillator was synchronized with the incoming carrier.

From this setting, any hand capacitance near the circuit would put it out of tune, resulting in a rising heterodyne whistle. Undoubtedly this phenomenon gave Theremin the idea for his instrument. To make it work, he built two oscillators operating on radio frequencies, one of which could be tuned (or detuned) by hand capacitance in relation to an electrode that projected from the instrument.

To complete the instrument, another electrode controlled the amplitude of the output signal. A carefully balanced bridge

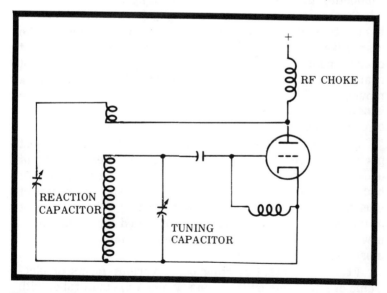

Fig. 4-1. The basic radio frequency amplifier stage of early radio days; the Theremin used a similar circuit with, of course, considerable refinement.

was disturbed by hand capacitance to another electrode, so that output amplitude could be modulated by moving the player's other hand. Thus one hand controlled the pitch and the other the loudness of the note. With a little practice, the player could evoke, by merely waving his hands in the air, quite musical sounds from the instrument. The sounds it produced resembled, more than enything, a musical saw as played by a bow. The words, "with a little practice," could have been taken from the marker's promotion: to a musician, accustomed to any regular form of instrument, it took at least as much effort to learn to play the Theremin as it did the first instrument he ever learned to play. Making it sound really musical was quite an acquired art.

To a musician accustomed to using his hands on something physical, such as a keyboard, the strings of an instrument, the valves of a wind instrument, etc., producing the music from a Theremin was curiously "intangible." Movement of his hands, in contact with nothing, produced musical sounds. In a sense, there may have been some similarity with the conductor's use of his hands; yet it was completely different from that, for the musician was not conducting the instrument but controlling it.

Further, the instrument was responsive to movement only in directions that changed the proximity of the hands to the respective electrodes. Movement in a direction that does not change the distance of the hand from its electrode does not change the pitch or intensity of the note. Thus, while extra movements could be thrown in for visual flourish for audience benefit, only certain movements actually developed a "feel" of controlling the instrument.

Nevertheless, from one point of view it was an almost perfect forerunner of modern synthesizers because it put under more complete control of the player, in a manner that had never been possible before, two of the basic parameters of musical notes: their pitch and their intensity. The movement of the player's hands completely controlled both, yielding a new freedom of expression, for which perhaps the world of music was not quite ready.

From a different starting point, various forms of electronic organs came on the scene. While a vacuum tube, with its associated tuned circuit to set the frequency was both less costly and less bulky than the organ pipe it replaced in a traditional organ, it would be considered extremely cumbersome or bulky in comparison with the corresponding electronics employed in today's organs. And the variety of sounds it could generate was quite limited by comparison with what different shaped organ pipes could yield. Electronic organs use different approaches to design nowadays. In those days, tuning was tricky so various approaches were aimed at achieving stability of tuning. Some manufacturers used a complete set of separate oscillators, perhaps several sets, one for every note on the organ. This required a very lengthy tuning process and stability was not easy to obtain.

Another approach, which always sounded more synthetic, used only 12 master oscillators, one for each note, A through

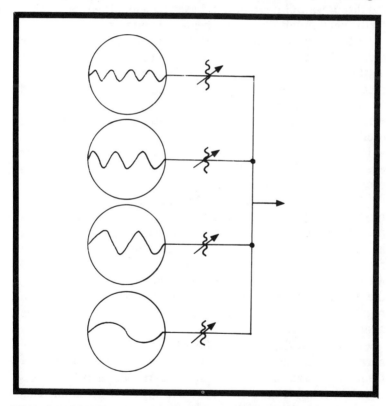

Fig. 4-2. This sketch illustrates the concept of tone synthesis. With this method, every note must have a synthesis network of which the one shown here is partial and typical. The method becomes extremely complex in execution, although simple in concept.

G, with sharps and flats, through the top octave of the organ. Notes for lower octaves were derived by electronic frequency dividers by halving the frequency of the same note from the octave above, again and again.

Still another approach was introduced by Hammond with tone wheels whose speed, and thus tuning, is controlled mechanically. Each note has a different tone wheel, but notes of the same name in successive octaves are mounted on the same shaft. So the organ has 12 rotating shafts, all turning at carefully controlled, different speeds. The magnetic output from the tone wheel (another approach, used by other makers, employs an electrical output from a capacitor-type wheel) is fed through amplification, synthesis, tone modification, and so forth, very much like any other electronic organ.

Functionally, with regard to tone modulation, organs divide into two main categories: those that modulate the tone at the source by controlling the generator, and those that modulate the tone after its generation. All organs that depend on a master frequency system, whether of the Hammond electro-mechanical type or those with a master set of 12 oscillators, are limited to the latter form. Modulating the tone at its source is limited to organs that provide an oscillator for every note. One exception to this is that vibrato can be provided as a modulation to a whole master system.

Apart from this basic difference in methods of tone modulation, three methods of varying the tone content of notes played can be used, separately or in combination. First, there is the frequency synthesis principle, or building up the required tone quality from component pure tones or sine waves (Fig. 4-2). The Hammond organs were, for many years, the leading exponent of this method, using drawbars to regulate the proportions of various harmonics mixed into the resulting sounds.

Second, in the selective formant method a tone rich in harmonics is generated, from which some groups of frequencies are emphasized and others depressed by electrical filtering (Fig. 4-3). Two basic types of harmonic-rich tones are predominantly used: the square wave and the sawtooth (Fig. 4-4). The square wave contains only odd harmonics and thus simulates the kind of sound generated by stopped organ pipes. Applying formants to this group of waves can simulate a whole range of stopped organ-pipe tones.

The sawtooth wave contains all the harmonics and thus simulates the kind of sound generated by open organ pipes. However it is not so easy to generate a sawtooth wave from frequency dividers which naturally generate the square form. But a number of organs by various means provide two complete families of tones by using these two basic forms with their respective formant filters.

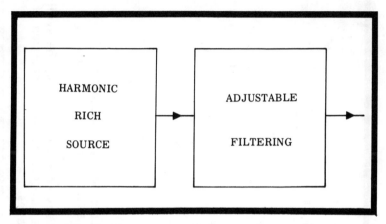

Fig. 4-3. The formant method takes a harmonic-rich tone and filters it down to the timbre required.

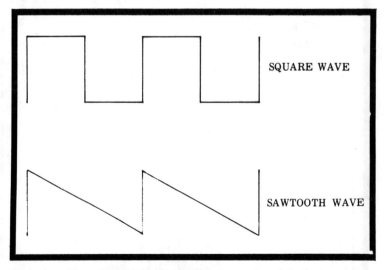

Fig. 4-4. Two basic forms of harmonic-rich tones commonly used in electronic organs.

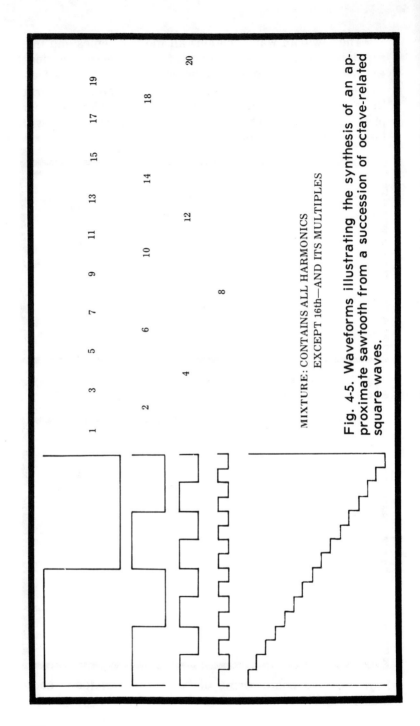

MIXTURE: CONTAINS ALL HARMONICS
EXCEPT 16th—AND ITS MULTIPLES

Fig. 4-5. Waveforms illustrating the synthesis of an approximate sawtooth from a succession of octave-related square waves.

A number of electronic organs produce a reasonable facsimile of a sawtooth waveform for this purpose by synthesis from successive octaves of the divider chain (Fig. 4-5). Thus the lowest octave square wave in the synthesis produces frequencies numbered 1, 3, 5, 7, 9, 11, 13, etc., where 1 is the fundamental and the other numbers represent those harmonics. The octave above this doubles these frequencies to produce those numbered 2, 6, 10, 14, 18, etc., which still leaves some out. Taking the next octave again fills in some of these gaps, such as 4, 12, 20, 28, etc. And another octave fills in 8 and its odd multiples. Then the only frequencies missing are those numbered 16 and its multiples. By mixing all these sets of frequencies at their correct amplitudes, the approach to a sawtooth is quite good. It actually sounds a little more brilliant, (less "rough") than a true sawtooth.

The third form of tone variation uses waveform control, as opposed to frequency selection of either kind used in the other two methods. Ideally, this could start with either a triangular or sawtooth waveform, from which an envelope forming network can make a variety of shapes. (Fig. 4-6.)

Electronic organs have used very little of the last named method and some organs combine more than one of these methods to some extent. They may use a master set of oscillators for some stops and individual oscillators for the whole organ on other stops. Or they may use synthesis for some stops and selective formants for others, perhaps combining the two for still others. The possibilities are virtually endless, within the limitations stated earlier. The waveform formant method must be applied note by note before the individual tones are combined. The frequency formant can be applied to a whole output after a group of tones in a harmony are mixed together (Fig. 4-7). Thus the choice between the methods possesses economic factors.

But organs are still somewhat 'straight-jacketed' with limitations traditionally inherent in a keyboard instrument. The flexibility inherent in a trombone or violin, for example, is completely beyond their capability. Perhaps I should modify that last statement to "has been," because there are ways to change that, although to my knowledge no organ maker has adopted any at this writing.

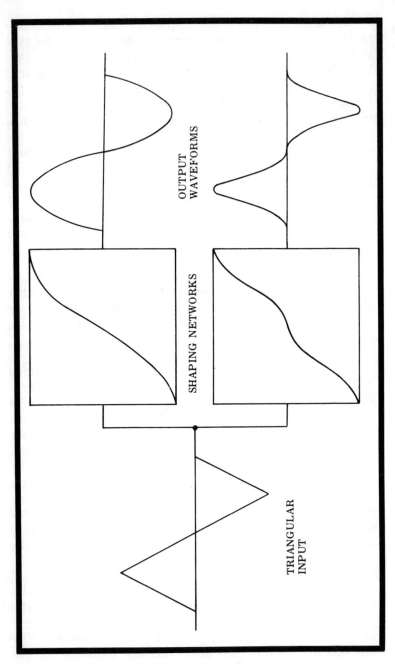

Fig. 4-6. A waveform formant, as opposed to frequency synthesis or formant, shapes individual tone waveforms.

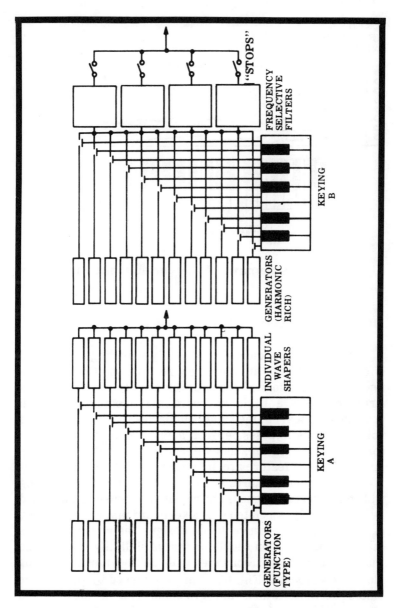

Fig. 4-7. Comparison of the two methods. With waveshaping every note must be shaped before the outputs are mixed (A). With frequency formant selection, notes may be mixed before applying to formant networks (B). With the first, every note needs every kind of shaper; with the second, the same formant network serves all notes.

87

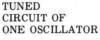

TUNED
CIRCUIT OF
ONE OSCILLATOR

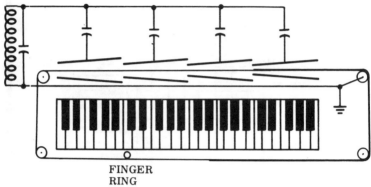

FINGER
RING

Fig. 4-8. Basic schematic of the variable-pitch feature of the Martinot.

MODERN DEVELOPMENTS

To meet this deficiency, incidentally exploiting the potential of electronic music into quite new realms, the Ondes "Martinot" and "Ondioline" were developed. Each of these instruments uses a basic keyboard arrangement, but with provision for leaving the rigid boundaries that a keyboard of notes normally imposes between notes. Each instrument has some elaborate features that will not explain in detail, merely give the unique feature around which the instrument is built.

The Martinot features a true glissando in which a sliding ribbon controls frequency. The ribbon movement is controlled by a finger ring associated with a keyboard that is used to play oscillators of more conventional design. The ribbon modifies the capacitance of an oscillator that is skillfully designed so that the note it plays coincides with the location of the ring along the keyboard (Fig. 4-8). This is achieved by shaping the plates between which the grounded ribbon moves, and changing the coupling of successive portions of the plate so that a greater effect on circuit capacitance is achieved in the upper octaves where the frequency change from note to note is a greater number of Hertz. A virtually linear relationship between capacitance and frequency is achieved by using a heterodyne principle, like the Theremin.

88

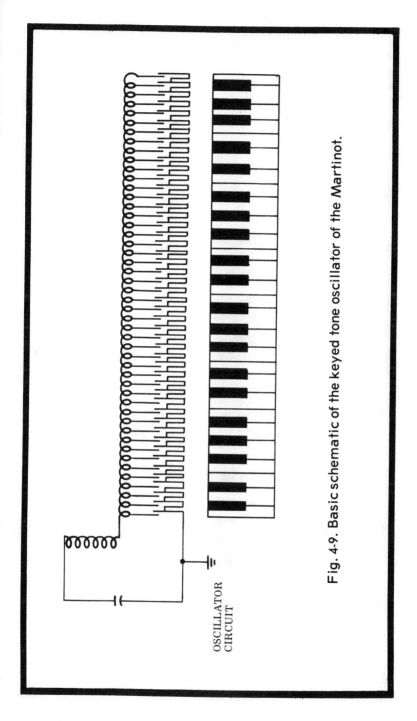

Fig. 4-9. Basic schematic of the keyed tone oscillator of the Martinot.

OSCILLATOR
CIRCUIT

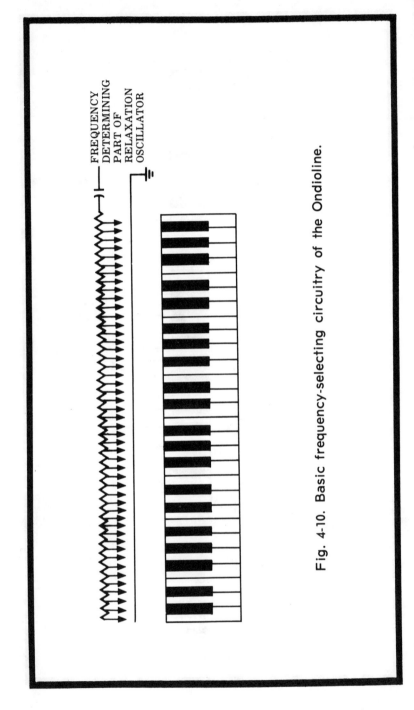

Fig. 4-10. Basic frequency-selecting circuitry of the Ondioline.

FREQUENCY
DETERMINING
PART OF
RELAXATION
OSCILLATOR

A fixed oscillator of 80 kHz is used in conjunction with a variable one that is lower than this by the note desired. Thus for concert A of 440 Hz, the variable oscillator has a frequency of 79,560 Hz. For the A below that, it is 79,780 Hz; for the one below that, 79,890 Hz. For an A above 440 Hz, it is 79,120 Hz, and for the one above that, 78,240 Hz. Stability is achieved by using temperature-compensated frequency-determining components.

For the fixed notes produced by the keyboard, another variable oscillator is used, with fixed tap on the oscillator coil. As this is a solo oscillator (it plays only one note regardless of how many keys may be pressed at once) the keyboard switching is arranged so that only one connection can be made, which may be either the lowest or highest key pressed, according to the designer's intent (Fig. 4-9).

In the Martinot, the lowest key pressed determines the note that plays. The Martinot was, in many respects, another instrument that enabled new flexibility to be demonstrated. The slide tone offered a unique flexibility, enabling the precision of the keyboard to be used with the individuality of glissando limited only by the player's skill in moving his finger.

An instrument quite different, but in many functional respects similar, is the Ondioline, also designed and built by Ondes from France. It uses a relaxation oscillator, instead of the heterodyne principle, and the variable resistance controls the frequency directly. In this case, no extra contacts are needed to ensure that only the correct note plays (Fig. 4-10). As the note is determined by the lowest resistance value (which fixes the highest note of the key depressed) any other keys pressed at the same time have no effect. The extra portions of resistance are short-circuited by the multiple key contacts.

The Ondioline also used frequency dividers and waveform synthesizers, in ways since adopted by many electronic organ makers. With skill in use of the controls of this instrument, it could almost be made to talk. The author remembers a demonstration by its inventor, in which he made the instrument "sing" the words used on the old Popeye cartoon movies, "I'm Popeye the sailor man..." For the moment I had to believe that was how the sound track for the movies was made; it was so near the same thing, produced entirely by a "musical" instrument.

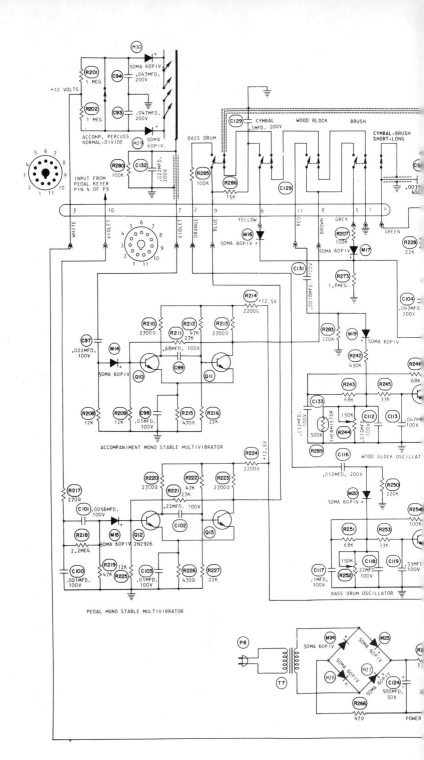

92

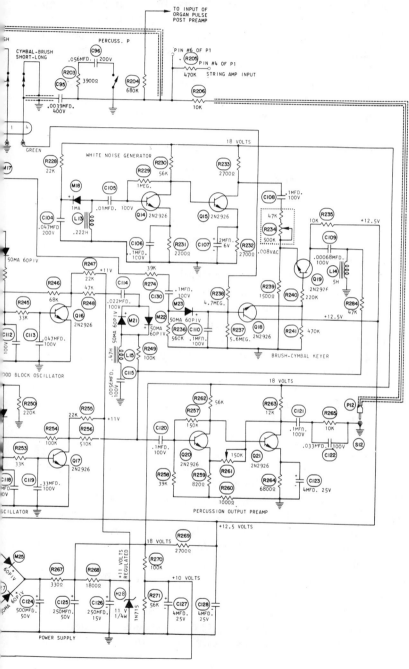

Fig. 4-11. Rhythm section schematic of an organ that uses the triggered method to follow the player's rhythm. (Courtesy Conn Organ Co.)

93

Like more recent synthesizers, this instrument was in considerable demand for what may be regarded as non-musical purposes: making odd sounds for commercials, or for cartoon film sound tracks. Directions in audio were changing, although as an industry the change was slow as usual. The real initiative was in the hands of a few inventors, while the phlegmatic body of audio men, including those who designed electronic organs, regarded instruments of this kind as a "passing phase" that would "never amount to anything!"

OTHER COMMONLY USED SYNTHESIS

Two more forms of traditional instruments have been generated entirely electronically and are often included as a feature in modern electronic organs. These instruments are usually grouped as percussive effects and use two kinds of electronic sources. One uses white noise as the basic generator. The other is a modified oscillator used to produce a synthesized sound that closely resembles a drum, wood block, or other nonperiodic percussives. The circuit may use any oscillatory arrangement: twin-T feedback, phase-shift feedback, or even a tuned circuit (although the last named have not been used for some years); the difference between a tone generator and this application is that the circuit is adjusted so it just does not oscillate.

The frequency at which it would oscillate determines the "tone" or pitch of the drum or block sound. Whether it has the character of a drum with a membrane that continues vibrating, or whether it has the short, staccato sound of a wood block, depends on the decay rate: how much short of oscillation the circuit is set. The sound is initiated simply by keying or otherwise changing the circuit suddenly from nonconducting into its operative mode. Fig. 4-11 shows a typical electronic tympani section of an electronic organ.

Snare drums, cymbals, and wire brush effects use the white noise generator to get the "sshhh" effect. For the snare drum the white noise is gated by the same signal that keys the resonant circuit to give the drum tone, with a time constant that cuts off the noise at the same rate as the oscillatory current decays. For the cymbals the noise is also gated and usually colored slightly by being passed through a broad-band filter. Additionally, a shock-excited oscillator, similar to that

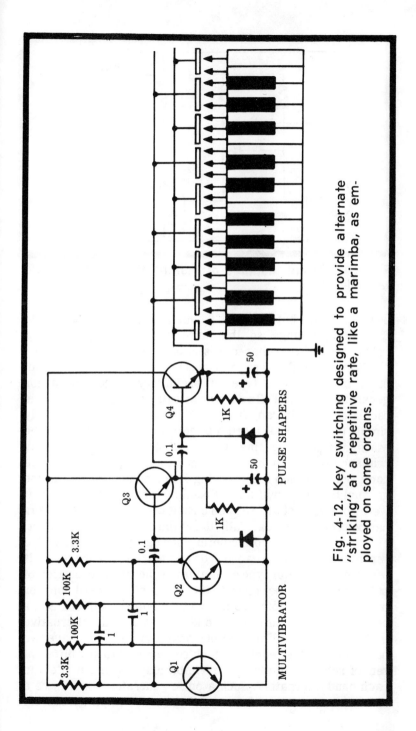

Fig. 4-12. Key switching designed to provide alternate "striking" at a repetitive rate, like a marimba, as employed on some organs.

95

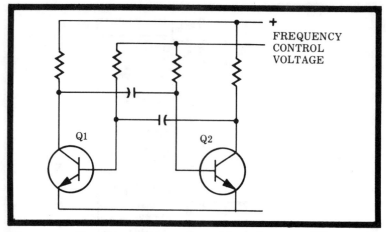

Fig. 4-13. Circuit capable of making the repetition rate variable.

used for drums but of higher frequency, is used additively to the gating voltage so the noise breaks through with a "shimmer" effect, characteristic of the cymbal.

Wire brush also uses some coloration in the form of broadband filtering. The type of oscillatory circuit used for generating tympani effects can vary almost as widely as basic oscillator circuits can. One thing is essential and relatively simple to achieve for a drum effect: the waveform should be essentially a dying sine wave. But getting an adequately realistic "strike" to the waveform may pose problems. It will come out as a plop if the keying is too sudden and if its too gradual the drum will hardly oscillate and will sound as if it were not struck at all. So each circuit used by various makers has been developed carefully to get the desired overall effect.

Another adjunct to the percussion section is the so-called repeater action which can also be applied to keyboard tones. It uses a multivibrator type oscillator to generate a succession of pulses that can either operate the gating of keyboard notes or pulse the output from drums or other tympani effects. Some organs provide more than one repeater with alternative methods of keying. For example, a multivibrator can have two outputs (Fig. 4-12) each of which can be used to key different sets of notes to simulate a marimba player using mallets in each hand alternately. Such a pulse generator would have a rate not very different from the single pulse output; it merely interlaces another set of pulses at the same speed. But for a drum roll, a faster pulse rate may be needed. This is just a matter of designing the pulse generator. In a transistor type pulse generator it is relatively easy to control the rate by adjusting the voltage used for base bias (Fig. 4-13).

A keying waveform should be a modified sawtooth. The output from a multivibrator can be square wave (from the collector or collectors) or a rather peculiar (from the musical viewpoint) sawtooth (Fig. 4-14). To convert this to a usable sawtooth, either a diode with or without an emitter follower can be interposed or the square wave output can be differentiated and then similarly used (Fig. 4-15). In the latter case there is a similar pulse of reverse phase midway between the ones used. If the tone is dead before this occurs, its presence will not matter. If the tone hangs on, still dying, until the next pulse repeats it, as is usually required, then the reverse polarity pulse must be suppressed.

The exact way in which these electronic effects are applied may use further electronic circuitry, short of the full synthesizer techniques which are discussed more fully in Chapter 6. Two methods are preferred by different organ manufacturers. One allows the greater freedom to the player, the other provides him with a sort of electronic rhythm, like a metronome, against which to play his melodic and harmony accompaniment.

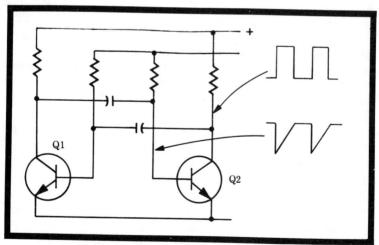

Fig. 4-14. Waveforms associated with this form of multivibrator do not include a good sawtooth.

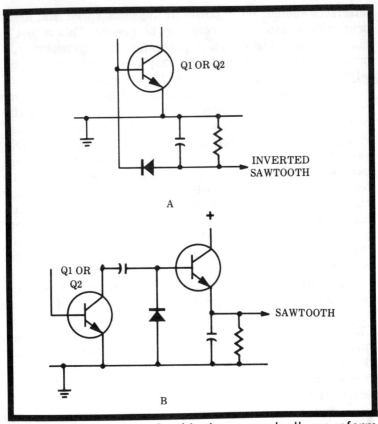

Fig. 4-15. Two ways of achieving a sawtooth waveform from the multivibrator: (A) using the base waveform and eliminating the "dent" with a diode; (B) using the square-wave output, differentiating it, and then using directional pulses to charge a capacitor which is discharged by a resistor or other current discharge device.

The first arrangement uses keying on one or both organ manuals and the foot pedals to provide a trigger action that keys the electronic drum or rhythm accompaniment every time a note in those ranks is played. Thus the bass drum may play every time a foot pedal is depressed and a side drum or brush may play every time the same pedal is released. Either the side drums, blocks, cymbals, according to the organist's choice, can then be keyed by the accompaniment manual or the solo manual, or both, every time one or more notes are played.

In earlier organs, these trigger signals were provided by extra contacts on all the key switches, but in more recent models all gating or keying is electronic, making the electrical switching operated directly by the keys much simpler. In these models electronic gating is used also to modulate the envelope of the notes played to give them the necessary percussive or other effects, possibly to provide sustain after each note is released. As keying voltages are available for this function, the same voltages can be picked off when needed to provide the trigger action for aperiodic percussive effects. Extra triggers are very easy to obtain when transistors to amplify small voltages or current are so small.

The other kind of percussive section uses an electronic timer to key the percussion, often with selectable rhythms (waltz, foxtrot, tango, cha-cha, etc., including some more modern ones, depending on the date the organ was made). These rhythms are measured out with electronic sequence timers that will beat out the same rhythm at the same tempo indefinitely (till the cows come home, as one man put it). Such a rigid tempo can be a help in learning to play strict tempo, but it can also be a little too rigid, making the music sound too "mechanical." This was one argument for the other type which takes its tempo strictly from the musician's playing.

However, the regularity of the rhythm generated electronically can be controlled by a simple variable resistance that changes the overall speed of the sequence. With this the play can slow the tempo for appropriate passages in a quite realistic way without losing the effect of the "beat," as he may when it takes its cue wholly from his playing. This latter type electronically sets up the requisite number of "beats to the bar" first, as a sequence, with all beats equal. Then selector switches pick off the necessary beats during the bar trigger to introduce the desired effects, bass drum, side drum, etc.

ADDING SUCH EFFECTS

The electronic organ enthusiast will often want to know whether he can add one or the other type of side effect to his organ. The strict tempo type is relatively easy to add to any organ. The first add-on of this type was the Wurlitzer "Side Man" which used a mechanical instead of electronic timing device, but otherwise functioned similarly. Many other units are now available that serve a similar purpose. They come with their own controls for speed, selecting rhythm, etc., and may have their own power amplifier or may rely on being connected into an existing (organ) power amplifier. If the organ does not have reverse power on one or the other amplifiers for such an extra input connection, it is not difficult to get an extra amplifier and speaker and make the "side man" completely separate from the organ.

For the other type that takes its cue from the organist, the organ must be designed with this kind of add-on in mind. It will usually have a set of output terminals specifically arranged for providing the trigger connections. If it does not, installation will probably involve adding a diode to every note on the organ, with a trigger bus. Even assuming this would work, after you have made all these extra connections, the soldering of that many diodes to connection points that may already be sensitive to heat could cause future trouble, even if it worked when first installed. The safest plan is to add such units only to organs that make specific provision for them.

TROUBLESHOOTING GUIDE

As one gets into more involved circuitry where electronics do the whole job, it becomes necessary to understand fully how the circuit is supposed to function before you tamper with trying to service one that has quit working. If it quit working, the oscillator is not functioning. As with any system, check the supply first. If correct supply voltages are reaching the oscillators and other circuits, but they do not work, then each circuit needs treating on the basis of how it is supposed to work.

If an oscillator does not work, in-circuit checking of its active elements and other components is the first step. If they appear to be in order, one method of finding out why an oscillator does not oscillate is the injection of signal at or near the frequency at which it should oscillate. If parameters are off somewhere, so it nearly oscillates but will not quite sustain oscillation, the injected signal will stimulate response at that frequency around the whole feedback loop. It will show that it is "trying." If something has failed completely, the response will be dead; signal will not circulate completely round the feedback loop. Other parts of the electronic system, in the various types of instruments treated in this Chapter, can be treated in conventional troubleshooting ways using the instrument's own oscillator as a test signal.

With instruments like the Martinot and Ondioline, it is possible that the instrument can go "out of tune." The solution in this case is to understand how tuning is achieved, as was explained earlier in the Chapter. Deduction based on what parts of the instrument are out of tune will help locate the fault. For example, if the glide tone on the Martinot is off register in one octave only, the series capacitor that modifies the capacitance reflected into the oscillator circuit could be off value for some reason. You will know which series capacitor to check or adjust.

If a single note misses its correct tuning in the Ondioline, where the tuning is accomplished by the sum of all the resistors for notes higher than the one keyed, the resistance error cannot be in the resistance chain because such an error would throw all notes below that point on the scale out of tune. In this case, there must be some spurious resistance, possibly due to a faulty contact in that particular note's keying. On the other hand, one note may be off tune badly, while those below it may also be out of tune but showing progressively less error until at the bottom of the scale it seems to be very close to in-tune. This would indicate that one resistor, for the note that is most seriously out of tune, has become faulty or off-value.

In a system with a mechanical source, such as the Hammond organ, reliability is high but error not impossible. If a generator shaft develops high friction in its bearings, the drive to that particular shaft may drag, allowing the pitch of notes of that name (A through G) to drop a little, relative to the rest of the scale. If the pitch of a single family of notes runs high, look for a reduced diameter in the driven pulley.

In the master oscillator systems, where electronic frequency dividers produce all the notes of a given name from one in the top octave of the instrument, the whole family may be off tune for a similar reason. In this case, tuning the note of that name in the top octave will correct matters. If such a tuning error is more than a semitone and there is no likelihood that the circuit has been tampered with by a novice turning a tuning screw, the probability is that some component in the oscillator circuit has become faulty. The whole master oscillator should be replaced and retuned to match the rest of the organ.

Tympani effects can develop similar troubles, but may not be quite so easy to trace because they do not oscillate actively. They must be stimulated by the appropriate trigger. If the oscillatory action is dead due to failure of a component, the characteristic tone will be missing and the output will be just a click when the electrical trigger voltage is received. Circuit tracing such devices requires techniques similar to those useful in oscillator circuits. Use a signal frequency the same as the drum is intended to emit and look for the point where the signal disappears.

Chapter 5

Amplifiers & Speaker Systems

A vital part of any electronic music system, whether the signal comes from a traditional or synthetic source, it the amplification and sound reproduction components. Although these amplifiers and speakers are usually part of the instrument, they function virtually just like any other amplifier and speaker system such as might be used for public address, for example. And yet amplifiers and speakers can be different. They do contribute something to the ultimate sound. And they do it in a variety of ways. First thing to consider is the signal to be amplified and how it can best be handled.

POWER REQUIREMENTS

Some solo instruments play one note at a time and the problem is simple: that of providing enough power to render that one note at its maximum, or at least at an adequate level or loudness. But most instruments as well as synthesizers play a whole harmony, in addition to the solo melody. And this complicates the question of how much power is needed.

Suppose a musical composition consists of a lead part or melody line with a peak level that, using a 16-ohm speaker of average efficiency, requires 40 watts drive. Assuming a sinusoidal waveform (as a matter of convenience for calculating; few musical waveforms actually are), this amounts to 25.3 volts RMS, or 35.8 volts peak. Now suppose the lead is accompanied by five harmony parts, each of which corresponds with a level one-tenth of the lead part (10 db down), or 4 watts, and a bass part at half the power level (3 db down) or 20 watts.

The obvious thing is to add the individual powers to arrive at a total power requirement: 40 + 5 x 5 + 20 or 80 watts. Note that figure. But all these 7 waveforms are of different frequency and thus will "cross" one another so that every now and then, say about every tenth of a second, all their peak waveforms could add by coinciding momentarily. To render the program undistorted, the amplifier must be able to handle these peaks when they come.

The peak voltage for the lead part is 35.8 volts (across the 16-ohm speaker). For each accompaniment part of 4 watts, the voltage is 8 RMS, or 11.3 volts peak, a total for the five (when they coincide) of 56.5 volts peak. And for the base, it is 17.9 volts RMS, or 25.3 volts peak. So the total peak when they all add will be 35.8 + 56.5 + 25.3 or 117.6 volts. Power rating is based on a nominal single sine wave. If the amplifier handles 117.6 volts peak, this as a sine wave would represent 860 watts peak or 430 watts average power. Therefore, the amplifier needs a rating of 430 watts to handle a total actual average power of 80 watts.

This problem can be compounded further in the loudspeaker system because, basically, diaphragm movement follows power drive. In fact, it can be aggravated in the loudspeaker because what the speaker diaphragm radiates is sound pressure. To create sound pressure the diaphragm has to move, and pressure is proportional to diaphragm velocity.

For a given peak velocity, total movement, or excursion, is inversely proportional to frequency. This means that bass notes involve much greater diaphragm movement than treble notes. And the loudspeaker, if the same diaphragm handles the whole frequency range, has to handle the peak movements at all frequencies, rather than the sum of the peak voltages.

Now suppose that 1 watt at 1,000 Hz corresponds with 0.003 inch peak movement of the speaker diaphragm. Suppose the lead part, or melody, is playing a note at 250 Hz, where 1 watt would correspond with 0.012 inch peak movement, and 40 watts would take the square root of 40 x 0.012 inch or 0.076 inch peak movement.

Then suppose that the accompaniment uses a 5-note spread where the average frequency is 150 Hz and the bass note is two octaves lower than the lead part, or 62.5 Hz. Each note in the 5-note group will require (on average) 0.020 inch movement per watt, or 0.040 inch movement for 4 watts; that means a 0.2 inch total movement for the 5-note group.

The bass note will require 0.048 inch movement per watt, or 0.214 inch movement for 20 watts. We have 0.076 inch movement for the lead part, 0.2 inch movement for the accompaniment group, and 0.214 inch movement for the bass note by itself. The total movement, when all coincide by moving together, will be 0.076 + 0.200 + 0.214 or 0.49 inch, nearly half an inch!

Referring this to equivalent power at 1000 Hz, it is 0.49 divided by 0.003, or 163 times the peak movement for 1 watt peak. This is equivalent to a power of 163 squared or 26,500 watts at 1000 Hz, which, of course, the speaker could not handle. But because the actual power delivered to the speaker is only the 80 watts referred to earlier, provided the voice coil is designed to get rid of most of this much power in heat (which is feasible in a large unit capable of this much voice coil movement), the speaker may survive,

But distortion may be unsatisfactorily high because of the large excursion. From this viewpoint, improvement can be effected by dividing the frequency range. Also, using separate amplifiers and speakers for separate parts of the music eases the situation, wherever this is feasible. Returning to our example, the lead part requires 400 watts; the accompaniment group could be accommodated by a 100-watt amplifier and the bass by another 20-watt amplifier, which is a lot less power than the 430-watt rating needed for one amplifier to handle the combined signal.

This brings us to a question that has been much discussed in high fidelity circles: whether to divide the signal before or after power amplification; that is, whether to use a single power amplifier feeding a number of speakers through crossover networks, or whether to use a frequency-dividing network first and then have each speaker system fed by its own power amplifier.

In a high fidelity system, the only way of separating signals is on a frequency basis. There is no way of separating frequencies in the same range that occupy the same channel. Thus, the bass note, with its 20 watts, could be separated from the remaining 60 watts (average) and that is all. But that 60-watt average would still require 92.3 volts peak, requiring an amplifier with 265-watt rating to handle it!

It would help the speaker situation a little more, reducing the movements to 0.276 inch and 0.214 inch. But if the lead part could use one amplifier and speaker, the accompaniment another and the bass a third, greater economy in audio power needs would be possible. And each of the speakers would be more tightly fed. To what extent this is possible depends on the instrument and whether the musical sections involved provide separate audio outputs. But making the separation where possible does result in a cleaner overall sound.

There are other aspects in which amplifiers may suit or not suit a musical application, and some interact with one another. We already discussed the relationship between peak and average power for various typical musical "signals." Now comes the question of how an amplifier behaves when a peak goes over the maximum level the amplifier will handle.

Some amplifiers merely clip off, or bend over, as waveforms larger than the ones they are meant to handle come in. When the waveform returns to the design level limits, the amplifier is performing perfectly again immediately. Other amplifiers take very little overload before something else happens from which they do not recover immediately.

For example, when level goes not too far above the top limit, clipping at some stage or other completely destroys gain: however much further the signal goes at the input to this stage, there is no corresponding signal or even a partly corresponding signal at the output from this stage; otherwise expressed, amplification at this stage ceases beyond this point on the waveform.

If the amplifier's gain has momentarily disappeared, so has its feedback, because there is no corresponding signal at the output to feed back. If the amplifier has, say, 20 db feedback normally, then this is gone and the input to the offending stage is suddenly magnified 10 times because feedback is no longer offsetting it.

This causes the clipping to assume almost a trigger action, making it push the offending stage far beyond normal overload with relative suddenness. The stage may be built to handle this and to shunt the excessive input signal away harmlessly. But more often, unless special care has gone into the design, the stage becomes blocked, somehow or other, and the bias or the supply voltage or current is pushed far beyond its normal operating range, so the stage is momentarily either saturated or cut off.

As a result, when the waveform returns to within its normal swing, that stage of the amplifier is still out of action, unable to amplify, and it may be anything from a few milliseconds to a fraction of a second, or even more than a

106

second, before amplification resumes, perhaps distorted at first, even for normal signals.

Now imagine a comparison, a real one that has happened many times: one amplifier can deliver, say, 25 watts undistorted; then distortion starts, and it may deliver 50 watts maximum but with distortion coming on relatively gradual; if you put in a peak of 10 times the input needed to give 25 watts output, it just distorts it and carries on normally as soon as the peak is gone.

Another amplifier is rated at 100 watts undistorted, which it really delivers. But beyond that it distorts fast, due to the trigger effect just discussed. It may give 120 watts with fairly high distortion, but if you put in more input than needed for that level the amplifier quits amplifying altogether and resumes only after this high signal level has been removed.

The incident where we first observed this involved a 15-watt and a 50-watt amplifier; amplifiers were not so highly rated then! A guitar player called our attention to it. The amplifier maker was demonstrating these two amplifiers to the player. The player complained that the 15-watt amplifier gave more output than the 50-watt amplifier. And when we listened to him play, we had to admit it was true.

Before we arrived on the scene to observe the comparison the amplifier maker had put each amplifier on his test bench and had his technician check them out; they both performed according to specifications. But put them back on the guitar and the effect was very definite: the 15-watt amplifier gave much more output than the 50-watter.

By now the technician was interested, possibly because it seemed someone doubted his measurements. He took the guitar and he made it seem as if the 50-watt amplifier gave at least as much, and possibly a little more, than the 15-watter. But he played the guitar very "carefully." As a technician, he watched the amplifier's overload points as he played, while the professional musician wanted his guitar to have a good, lusty "attack."

There was the difference. This initial attack by the professional meant he could not work at or anywhere near the 50-watter's full output, while the 15-watter handled full output. This distinction between amplifiers is probably more important for musical instrument work than for any other use. In recording or hi-fi reproduction, peaks are carefully taken care of to avoid this kind of problem. In public address work, acoustic feedback is usually the prime problem, so overload never gets in the way.

Another difference between amplifiers is subtle in a different way. This concerns what is known as its damping factor. An amplifier is designed to deliver its output into a load of specified impedance, say, 16 ohms. But this says nothing about the internal impedance of the amplifier output. It could be a small fraction of the load, such as 0.1 ohm, which represents a damping factor of 16. Or it could be higher than the load value, such as 80 ohms, which represents a fractional damping factor.

Either amplifier's internal output impedance can deliver its output into the same load just as effectively, all the while the load operates at its nominal value. But loudspeakers have impedance that have a nasty habit of departing materially from their nominal value. Suppose the 16-ohm speaker has an impedance that is 16 ohms at 800 Hz but rises to 120 ohms at 110 Hz, and rises again at frequencies above about 1500 Hz. And suppose the amplifier receives the same input voltage at all frequencies for a test run at a level so that it will never overload, even with the loudspeaker for a load.

Assume the output voltage is 10 volts across the 16-ohm impedance at 800 Hz. When the frequency is changed to 110 Hz, the voltage rises less than 10 percent on the amplifier with a damping factor of 16, actually to about 10.6 volts. But on the amplifier with the fractional damping factor and an internal impedance of 80 ohms, the voltage will rise to about 36 volts. The voltage will also rise at higher frequencies.

Thus, using the same loudspeaker but different amplifiers, each of which measures quite flat under test conditions, the one with the fractional damping factor will produce more than a 10 db peak at 110 Hz with increasing peaks at the high-frequency end in comparison with the one that has a higher damping factor.

From this you might assume that a high damping factor is good. In general, it is. But it can also be useful to have a lower damping factor under certain circumstances: it can accentuate certain bass and treble frequencies quite simply. Remember that in electronic music work, there may not be a right and wrong way: what you want is the best effect.

CHOICE OF SPEAKERS

In a high fidelity system, the objective of the speaker is to reproduce every kind of sound as faithfully as possible. The loudspeaker should not add any tone character of its own. But for a musical instrument amplifier system, the same comment does not apply. A guitar amplifier, for example, is always reproducing guitar music, not all kinds of instruments.

Just as the careful design of a traditional guitar body introduces resonances that add timbre to the music it produces, so does the choice of a suitable loudspeaker to go with the amplifier (even one specially developed for the job perhaps) provide the capability of faithful reproduction. Many musicians have sought to improve their system by using a "better" speaker, meaning a high quality, high fidelity model. They have been disappointed with the result because the "inferior" one they already had was deliberately chosen to give a desired effect. If you look at a loudspeaker belonging to a musical instrument amplifier, do not be in too much of a hurry to condemn it as "crummy." It may have been chosen for a good reason.

For synthesizers, this is not true. A synthesizer generates a waveform that can be mixed directly with any other musical effects without speaker or microphone. To hear it, you need a loudspeaker, and it should be of high quality, a high fidelity model, to show what the program will sound like played on a system of maximum fidelity.

MATCHING

Another matter requiring attention, and which may involve technicians who deal with musicians, is that of matching. A system will naturally come with amplifier and speakers that match. But a customer or musician may want to add extra loudspeakers for one reason or another. This can involve a matching problem. The system may come with jacks or external terminals for connecting outside speakers, either as alternatives, or in addition to the ones that came with it.

Speaker units come in several impedances. For high fidelity stereo applications, the common impedances are 4, 8, and 16 ohms. For commercial radio and television receivers, 1.35 ohms was for a long time standard. For intercom systems, 45 ohms has been a standard. And for solid-state equipment, with speakers built in, impedances may be tailored to suit the amplifier.

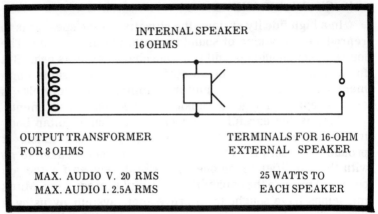

INTERNAL SPEAKER
16 OHMS

OUTPUT TRANSFORMER
FOR 8 OHMS

TERMINALS FOR 16-OHM
EXTERNAL SPEAKER

MAX. AUDIO V. 20 RMS
MAX. AUDIO I. 2.5A RMS

25 WATTS TO
EACH SPEAKER

Fig. 5-1. A typical amplifier output-speaker coupling circuit.

Power will divide between different loudspeakers connected to an amplifier output on the basis of their respective impedances and how they are connected. And the total amount of power will depend on the correctness of matching, effected by all the loudspeakers connected in whatever way to the amplifier. Suppose, for example, that an amplifier is designed to operate into an 8- to 16-ohm load and is provided with a 16-ohm loudspeaker system with the intent that an external 16-ohm speaker connected additionally would reduce the load impedance to 8 ohms (Fig. 5-1). Now suppose that an external speaker with an impedance of 1.35 ohms is connected.

First, the combination of 1.35 ohms and 16 ohms in parallel makes the total load on the amplifier an inpedance of 1.35 x 16 divided by 17.35 or 1.25 ohms. If the amplifier is designed to deliver 25 watts into 16 ohms and 50 watts into 8 ohms (the latter being optimum matching), it will probably deliver only 9.4 watts into 1.25 ohms before serious distortion sets in.

About 16 divided by 17.35 of this 9.4 watts, or 8.7 watts, will be delivered to the 1.35-ohm unit outside, while the 16-ohm unit will receive only 1.35 divided by 17.35 of the total, or about 700 milliwatts, in place of the usual 25 watts! If the 1.35-ohm unit is used as an extension speaker, its 8.7 watts is somewhat less than the expected 25 watts, but the 700 milliwatts to which the internal speaker drops is a more drastic change.

Series connection, which involves a little changing of connections internally, would improve this situation. It can be

110

achieved by using a shorting jack to enable the external unit to be inserted in series with the internal one (Fig. 5-2). Now, because the impedance is raised from 16 to 17.35 ohms, the total power will probably drop from 25 watts to about 23 watts, of which about 21 watts will appear at the internal 16-ohm speaker and 1.8 watts at the external 1.35-ohm unit.

Of the two choices, this is probably better. But if more even distribution of power between two such disparate units is required, something else needs doing. The correct thing would be to provide the 1.35-ohm unit with a matching transformer to

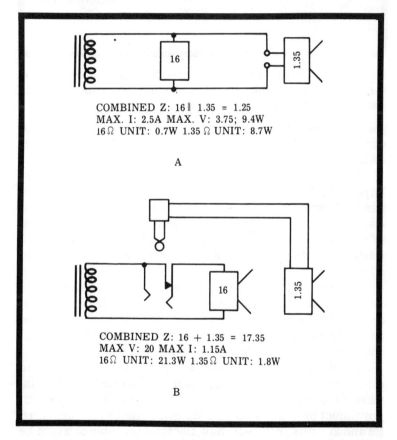

COMBINED Z: 16 ‖ 1.35 = 1.25
MAX. I: 2.5A MAX. V: 3.75; 9.4W
16Ω UNIT: 0.7W 1.35 Ω UNIT: 8.7W

A

COMBINED Z: 16 + 1.35 = 17.35
MAX V: 20 MAX I: 1.15A
16Ω UNIT: 21.3W 1.35Ω UNIT: 1.8W

B

Fig. 5-2. If the external speaker has an impedance of 1.35 ohms instead of 16 ohms, here are two possibilities for connection: A, following the book, without reference to the fact that the impedance is wrong; B, changing the circuit so a series connection is used.

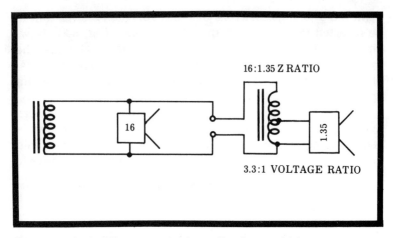

16:1.35 Z RATIO

16

1.35

3.3:1 VOLTAGE RATIO

Fig. 5-3. A better or ideal method would be to use a matching transformer to make the 1.35-ohm loudspeaker look like 16 ohms.

convert its impedance to 16 ohms, in which case the amplifier can be used as it was designed, both units would receive 25 watts, or close to it (Fig. 5-3).

However, loudspeakers can mismatch in more than just impedance. For example, the 1.35-ohm unit may not be built to handle 25 watts of power. Possibly its maximum would be 10 watts. In that case the only way to limit the operation would be to turn the volume down, so both speakers receive only 10 watts each. which is wasteful when the internal one is capable of handling 25 watts.

If the matching transformer used with the 1.35-ohm unit is designed to provide a match for 40 ohms, as well as for the 16-ohm tap, this would help even more. Now the 16-ohm unit can be fed its customary 25 watts and the 40-ohm load in parallel with it will accept only the required 10 watts (Fig. 5-4).

If the transformer can step up the 1.35-ohm impedance to something like, say, 4 ohms, it could be inserted in series instead of parallel (Fig. 5-5), which would still be an improvement over the simple series connection which delivered 1.8 and 21 watts (Fig. 5-2). Now the total impedance would be 20 ohms, the total power would drop to 20 watts, but 4 watts would go to the 4-ohm (with transformer) unit and 16 to the 16-ohm units.

A speaker matching transformer usually has multiple taps, the important thing being the ratio available. For example, a design may provide 4, 8 and 16 ohms only. If the 1.35-ohm unit is connected to the 4-ohm tap (Fig. 5-6), the 8-ohm tap will match it to 2.7 ohms and the 16-ohm tap to 5.4 ohms.

That is in theory. In practice, winding resistance will be on the high side for these lower impedances (1.35 ohms is lower than the 4 ohms for which it id designed). The 8-ohm tap will look like nearer to 4 ohms and the 16-ohm tap nearer to 8 ohms. And because of this extra winding resistance, efficiency will be poor: only about two-thirds of the power will reach the speaker unit. Thus, using the 8-ohm tap in the connection of Fig. 5-5, the transformer would receive 4 watts, of which about

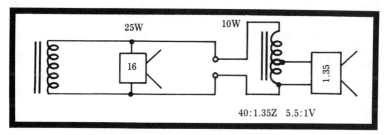

Fig. 5-4. The connections in Figs. 5-3 and 5-4 do not consider power ratings. If the external speaker will handle only 10 watts instead of 25 watts, here is one way to arrange it so that the internal speaker receives 25 watts and the external one 10 watts.

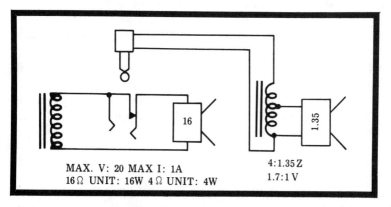

Fig. 5-5. If some change in impedance can be effected by using a transformer, but a change which is not the ideal, this method may be better than either direct connection of Fig. 5-2.

113

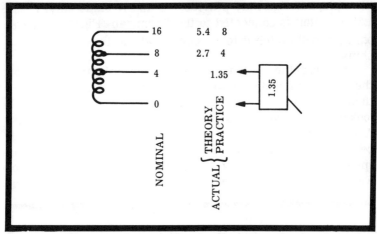

Fig. 5-6. The numbers indicate the degree of mismatch that occurs when the nominal impedances provided by an available transformer do not agree with the actual impedances used.

2.7 watts will reach the speaker unit. On the other hand, using the 16-ohm tap, the total impedance is 24 ohms, taking 0.83A. The 16-ohm internal unit will receive about 11 watts, while the external transformer will receive about 5.5 watts, of which about 3.5 watts will reach the speaker; that is almost 1 watt better than the other connection, although the internal speaker drops to not much more than half its former power.

Treating that example at some length shows the method of figuring that can be used. The variety of possibilities that may be encountered is virtually infinite. The method is the same: figure out the best compromise after taking into account all the factors. Two things need to be considered in every case: best overall matching to make the most power available from the amplifier, and a desirable distribution of power between the units that share it.

INPUT MATCHING

The input to a power amplifier must match the signal fed into it for both impedance and level. Many musical instrument amplifiers are integrated, as a matter of convenience, so the inputs match the instruments, which are amplified and combined to feed the requisite power amplifier sections.

114

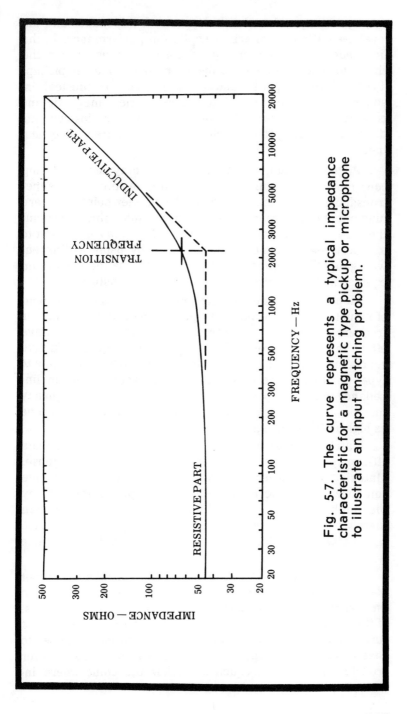

Fig. 5-7. The curve represents a typical impedance characteristic for a magnetic type pickup or microphone to illustrate an input matching problem.

115

Again, in problems of this type, both impedance and the level need attention to achieve optimum performance. In the first place the amplifier input impedance must match the characteristic impedance of the microphone or other pickup. Types of microhpones and pickups used for musical instruments fall principally into two categories: magnetic and ceramic. Of course, the purely electronic instruments discussed in the previous chapter have a purely electrical input.

Magnetic pickups and microphones may use a moving coil, moving armature (moving iron), or moving magnet transducer. From the transducer design viewpoint there are fundamental differences, but from the matching viewpoint they are more similar than different. Each may be wound to any desired impedance (within limits) by using a different wire gauge and number of turns, or it may be matched to an equivalent but different impedance by a transformer.

All possess a basic resistive impedance with a component of inductance that becomes the predominant factor at higher frequencies (Fig. 5-7). The frequency at which the inductive effect takes over from the resistive (i.e., where inductive reactance is equal to resistive impedance) varies from type to type, but this is the only essential difference from an impedance-matching point of view. The transistion frequency may be as low as (or even lower than) 1000 Hz. It may also be as high as (or even higher than) 10,000 Hz.

Matching, with this type of device, principally affects efficiency of transfer (gain) and high-frequency response. Matching into a lower impedance load, down to the resistive component of its internal impedance if the power absorbed by the amplifier input is utilized for gain purposes rather than merely being dissipated in a passive resistance, will increase sensitivity or gain. Matching into resistances below this value will again lose gain.

To illustrate what this means, let's consider the input stage at Fig. 5-8. With a controlled beta of 20, a 100-ohm emitter resistor will present an input impedance of 2,000 ohms. If the pickup or microphone also has a resistive component of its own impedance of 2,000 ohms, or is transformer matched to that value, the arrangement will result in maximum power transfer (gain) for frequencies below the point where inductance becomes significant.

VALUE OF R	INPUT Z	HF ROLL-OFF FREQUENCY	STAGE GAIN
100	2000	4000	18
300	6000	8000	6
700	14000	16000	7.5

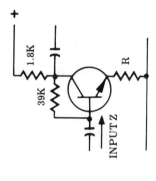

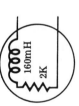

PICKUP OR MICROPHONE

Fig. 5-8. Component values to match the input impedance of an amplifier to a magnetic pickup or microphone.

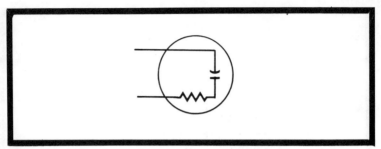

Fig. 5-9. The impedance of a ceramic type pickup or microphone is primarily capacitive.

Now suppose that the microphone's internal inductance is equivalent to 160 millihenries, which puts the frequency where it is 2,000 ohms reactive at about 2,000 Hz. Applying this transducer to an input loading of 2,000 ohms will associate the 160 millihenries with 4,000 ohms total, putting the 3 db high-frequency roll-off point at 4,000 Hz.

For some applications, this may be satisfactory. But if the upper harmonics of sounds to be picked up are required, a high roll-off frequency may be desirable. To extend it to 8,000 Hz. For example, the external loading impedance, presented by the amplifier, should be 6,000 ohms to make the total 8,000 ohms. To extend it to 16,000 Hz, the external loading impedance needs to be 14,000 ohms. Be nature of things, such an extension of response is accompanied by a loss of gain at frequencies below the point where the inductive reactance becomes effective. The table on Fig. 5-8 completes the comparison.

The other predominant kind of transducer uses a piezo-electric ceramic to convert mechanical (and thus acoustical, in the case of a microphone) movement into an electrical output. The electrical properties of such a device resemble mostly a simple capacitance (Fig. 5-9). The resistive element is small enough to be negligible for all practical purposes. As the device produces a voltage proportional to the deflection of the ceramic element from its normal position and presents an electrical source impedance equivalent to a capacitor, it may be represented as a voltage generator with a series capacitor.

Loading this device with a resistance causes a low-frequency roll-off. The higher the resistance value of the input load impedance, the lower in frequency the low-frequency roll-off occurs. Some specifications for devices of this type give the effective capacitance. Others specify a load impedance with a corresponding response characteristic.

Suppose the recommended load impedance is 2 megohms, which produces a low-frequency roll-off at 80 Hz. This sets the value of the capacitance at 0.001 mfd, because a 0.001-mfd capacitor has a reactance of 2 megohms at 80 Hz. If it is loaded with 1 megohm, the roll-off frequency will rise to 160 Hz; if it is loaded with 4 megohms, the roll-off frequency will drop to 40 Hz.

The ideal input device to use with this type of transducer is an FET because it is a voltage rather than a current input device. With regular current-amplifying transistors, finding a high enough impedance is a struggle. Lowering the input impedance increases input stage gain but it reduces the sensitivity of the transducer correspondingly, as well as deteriorating the bass response.

As with output circuits, not only are gain and frequency response important but levels are, too. The amplifier may be equipped with controls to adjust gain, but unless the level of the output from the transducer suits the level for which the amplifier input was designed, performance is deteriorated before any adjustment of gain can be made (Fig. 5-10).

If the level is too high for the amplifier input circuit, distortion may occur before the gain can be controlled. If the level is too low, extra gain may be available, but background noise or hum could spoil the performance.

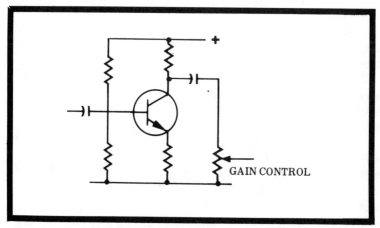

Fig. 5-10. When the gain control is located after the first stage, overload and noise problems are more likely.

FEEDBACK

Levels are also important relative to another possibility: feedback, which can be electrical, mechanical or acoustic. Excessive gain, using a common supply source in which there is always some common impedance, can result in electrical feedback and resultant instability. Amplifiers are usually designed so that they remain stable under all normal operating conditions. But if extra amplification is provided, e.g., by a preamplifier powered from the main amplifier, electrical feedback can occur through the common supply source. This can be avoided by additional decoupling or by use of a separate power supply for the auxiliary amplifier.

Electrical feedback of this kind occurs because the power supply, used by the whole of the amplification (the original and that added as extra), possesses an impedance that couples from the higher level signal in the original amplifier back to the lower level signal in the extra stages. Increasing the decoupling in the supply feed to the extra stages may eliminate the feedback, but as in the nature of things, there is a limit. When more than a certain amount of gain, dependent on the internal resistance of the supply and the levels involved, is used, the amount of decoupling required to prevent feedback reaches a point where the capacitor value needed rises very fast. It is not economical to go this road, if a capacitor such as 10,000 mfd is not adequate. Then the best answer is to use a completely separate power supply with adequate smoothing.

Mechanical feedback is much less likely to occur in transistorized amplifiers than it was in tube amplifiers. All tubes were, to some extent, mechanically microphonic, colloquially called "pongy." Too much gain, following a low-level input stage, could result in sound waves or vibrations from the output causing electrical inputs to be generated in the input stage tube due to mechanical vibration of its electrodes.

In earlier days, the only way to overcome microphonicity was to employ shock-absorbing mountings. Some extremely resilient tube sockets were designed with this objective and sometimes the tubes were surrounded with sound absorbent material and the whole amplifier assembly resiliently mounted in addition. Attention to tube design also reduced the microphonicity of tubes and made less of this elaborate precautionary measure necessary. But solid-state devices (transistors and other newer active elements) have virtually eliminated microphonicity as a problem.

Acoustic feedback refers more specifically to amplified sound finding its way back to the sound pickup device or microphone, and thus causing a similar form of instability or howl. The solution to this is usually the choise of a different form of sound pickup that is more sensitive to the source being picked up and less sensitive to acoustic waves coming from outside the instrument.

However, do not overlook the possibility of a microphonicity, similar to that experienced at one time with tubes. Although solid-state devices are free from this problem, pickups that serve as microphones are not. They may be primarily intended to detect a certain kind of vibration, such as that of a steel guitar string. But other vibratory movements that similarly disturb the magnetic circuit of the pickup can also yield an output and cause microphonicity.

A clue to the existence of this condition is an overly sensitive wood guitar frame. Of course, any time a guitar is jarred, slapped, or whatever, the strings vibrate, and the sound of their vibration will be picked up. But if the sound of the wooden frame vibrating is also picked up, something is wrong. Maybe the coils are loose, or move with the baseboard, while the magnetic material tends to stay still. This kind of pickup should be rigid, no internal movement. Then the only thing that will produce an output is the movement of the strings relative to the pickup.

TROUBLESHOOTING AMPLIFIERS AND SPEAKER SYSTEMS

Amplifier and speaker systems used with musical instruments often take a terrible beating, in just being toted around, apart from the vibration they sustain when the equipment is played at the levels most teenage groups seem to insist upon. As this is written, it seems that teenage music is not played for sound, but for feeling. And this punishment for people is also punishment for equipment. Vibrations can jar connections loose so that speakers may cease to make connection for no other reason. Check for continuity of the voice coil and its connections. If the trouble is intermittent, it may take some prodding, pulling, or twiddling to find the bad connection. All too often, it will act up when its in its case, going on and off at intervals. Then when you remove the unit from the case to try to discover the fault, it works perfectly; nothing will make it misbehave! It may also work when you first return it to its case and only start repeating the aggravation after it has been in its case a day or two!

There are no real short cuts to finding such problems. Look for bad connections, a broken wire inside the insulation, etc. You may find it that way. Good luck! Look for wires that stretch indicating that there is a break inside the insulation, where the insulation is all that holds it together. Pulling on wires is often a way to find an intermittent fault, for this reason.

But pulling can sometimes momentarily remedy a dubious soldered joint, too. If the joint is one where the connection is mechanical as well as electrical, where the lead was twisted round the lug before it was soldered, maybe the joint has deteriorated electrically and no solder any longer makes a permanent connection. However, the joint is impossible to break mechanically without melting the solder. In this case, pulling the lead may cause the connection to remake an electrical but nonpermanent contact.

If this happens, resolder the questionable joint carefully. If the joint is located where solder getting "out of bounds" could cause trouble, extra care is needed. Maybe the joint should be carefully dissected by cutting the connection away until it can be soldered without using excessive heat from the solder gun; then completely remake the joint.

Occasionally a voice coil will go bad, but this is easy to spot with a continuity check. Sometimes the amplifier may quit temporarily for some reason. This, too, could be an intermittent contact, or a protection circuit could be acting up. Modern high-power amplifiers use overload circuits that electronically shut off the input to the power output stage or its drive. A defect in such circuits can either have them triggering off too readily, or result in a tendency to stay off too long or maybe altogether.

Modern high-power amplifiers use transistors with big heat sinks, built like radiators, which they really are. If they blow, an in-circuit test will usually find the trouble.

Such equipment comes in an ever-changing variety of physical designs, so you will often encounter something you have not seen before. It is always better if you have a service manual on the equipment, or perhaps a sheet, or at least a schematic. If you do not, you have to do some circuit tracing and try to figure out how it works as best you can.

Do not get too involved without knowing what you are doing. Some equipment has a warranty. And whether it does or not, the manufacturer's official service agency will service it less expensively if he finds the fault untampered with. If he finds someone has been "poking around" he must look for extra troubles the prodder may have unwittingly caused.

Even if you know how the circuit is supposed to work, or if you have a schematic, do not assume the schematic and the equipment should agree exactly. Often makers will change the design in some small way without altering the schematic to correspond. So you have to approach every strange problem on the assumption that it once worked; therefore, you have to find a fault; something that has happened to stop if from working.

The last remark may seem obvious. But in modern compact circuits, a breakdown of insulation, for instance, may look as if the place never had insulation. So you will be tempted to conclude, after examining the whole thing thoroughly without finding any evidence of damage, that the thing never could have worked. It may take a little deduction to discover that a surface which now appears to be conducting was originally coated or treated in some way to render it an insulator. And when you have made the deduction, you may need to affirm it by referring the question to the manufacturer.

And do not overlook the possibility that the "failure" may not be electrical or electronic in the accepted sense. The owner or user may have changed something that altered the previously successful arrangement. A different amplifier-speaker combination (changing one or other) may still "work." Only later does the user become aware of something wrong, due to the overload effect, or something due to a change in damping factor, something that was not immediately apparent when the change was made.

This kind of problem may call for astute deduction on your part. Many users will swear it worked all right when they first made the "switch." And they will probably forget to tell you they even made the switch, because they have probably made up their minds that a definite fault had "developed," which is your responsibility to trace.

Chapter 6

Synthesizers

The original synthesizer work was carried out by Dr. Harry Olson of RCA Labs, many years ago now, using what, by today's standards, would be regarded as rather crude components. However, his methods were sound and the components he used were the best, the most advanced types available to him at the time. He built most of the equipment specially at the Lab, and the work he did paved the way for the tremendous progress that has followed. Fig. 6-1 shows most of the original RCA synthesizer.

First he set down the variables to any musical tone, enabling it to be identified from other tones. The first variable is **pitch**, which depends on frequency. Next comes **loudness**, which depends on intensity or amplitude. Third comes a quality called **timbre**, which depends on the overtone or harmonic structure.

With those three qualities, which have been long recognized, all we have identified is some form of steady tone that could come from the lab oscillator but which does not necessarily sound musical. What gives a tone qualities more readily recognized as musical are its transient properties: the way it starts to play, how it performs while it is playing, and how it finishes playing.

This fact leads to a study of the waveform envelope properties of **growth**, **sustain**, and **decay** (Fig. 6-2). But beyond those simple distinctions there are yet more variations, such as **tremolo**, **vibrato** and **portamento** (a tone gliding smoothly from one pitch to another) that have quite a pronounced effect on musical quality.

Dr. Olson also worked with another class of sound, derived not from a specific note generator, modified in the ways mentioned above, but from white noise - random sound -

Fig. 6-1. This original RCA synthesizer occupied an entire laboratory. (Courtesy RCA)

passed through various filters, and modulated in amplitude or frequency content. This proved useful for simulating some of the precussive sounds, such as the cymbal, the wire brush, etc.

Dr. Olson's synthesizer used punched tape (Fig. 6-3) to program his equipment, note by note, to build up a musical program. Rolls and rolls of punched tape were fed into the equipment and the resulting sounds were recorded on multitrack disc (magnetic recording was not sufficiently developed when he started).

Finally, the various tracks on the disc were rerecorded onto a single track to make the whole musical composition. Because of the relative inefficiency of the components he used, and because the very bulk of the equipment in those days limited the degree of sophistication he could achieve, the results were disappointing to some.

Reaction to those early demonstrations probably depended on the individual's viewpoint. Musicians and

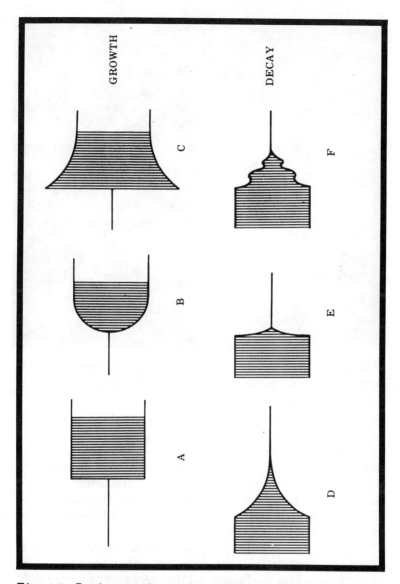

Fig. 6-2. Basic sound envelope criteria as established in early analysis: A, B, and C represent different growth patterns for a tone. A, sudden, like switching on; B, with some delay; C, with overshoot to give a percussive effect. Between the growth and decay comes a period known as "sustain." D, E and F illustrate different decay patterns for a tone: D, relatively slow decay; E, faster decay; F, decay with irregularity.

127

Fig. 6-3. Close-up of the punch-tape system used to program the original RCA synthesizer. (Courtesy RCA)

electronic engineers alike were astounded because such musical sounds could be heard in the reproduced sound. Their reaction reminded me of a musician listening to a very old, acoustical recording to assess the performance of an orchestra who made the recording, perhaps in the nineteenth century. As I listen, I can hardly hear anything for the background noise and scratch, but my musician friend is listening to the musicians of another age!

So it was with those early demonstrations with synthesizers. Imaginative musicians and engineers alike could hear the sounds of the future. All that background noise would disappear as had the scratch associated with the acoustic recordings made during the last century. They were not listening to the background but to the promised sounds of the future. Dr. Olson was a pioneer!

But, just as the primitive Theremin took time to learn to play, the modern synthesizers require the development of a whole new technique or proficiency. And meanwhile, engineers are using their imagination to make the whole thing even more flexible and easier for a musician to use. So very many things are possible and so few of them have yet been tried or done.

INGREDIENTS OF A SYNTHESIZER

The development of functional integrated circuit packages is what really liberated synthesizer development from the impediments that had previously hampered progress. Instead of having to build every part of a synthesizer from the ground up, with literally thousands of parts, it can now be put together from packages, each of which serves a complete function, with any degree of precision that may be desired or necessary.

Earlier synthesizers started with a feedback oscillator intended primarily to generate a sine waveform, because the frequency-controlling elements of the circuit discriminate on the basis of a sine-wave frequency (Fig. 6-4). Then, if other waveforms were required, as they usually were, this waveform was either distorted and then shaped by formants, or the requisite waveform was synthesized from basic sine

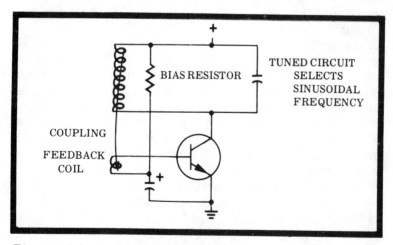

Fig. 6-4. A typical tuned-circuit sine-wave oscillator circuit illustrating the characteristics. Many other forms exist, but all have the same essential properties. Successful progress in synthesizer development largely coincided with abandonment of this type of oscillator.

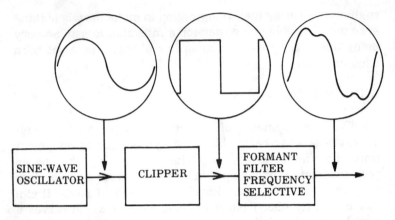

Fig. 6-5. These waveforms illustrate the formant method of producing a wave of required timbre in the days when sine-wave oscillators were still used.

waves. Most usually the former process was adopted because it was simpler (Fig. 6-5).

These methods prevailed until the advent of the function generator and more widespread development of the relaxation oscillator (multivibrator). These generate basic sawtooth, square, or triangular waveforms and other forms are derived from that (Fig. 6-6).

To produce a sine wave, using the same frequency-controlling elements (that we will discuss in a moment) the wave is made triangular and then put through a function generator that shapes it to a close aproximation of a sine wave. With relatively few components a sine wave of high purity can be generated this way and the precise control of its frequency and amplitude is far easier than with the old frequency tuning method. Perhaps we should show the difference more specifically.

In a basic sine-wave generator of the old style, oscillation occurs by selective feedback, of which a dozen or more varieties are available. Such oscillators all have one characteristic in common: they feed back one specific, sinusoidal frequency from output to input.

If the amount of feedback is slightly increased, the waveform builds up until distortion sets in. If the amount of feedback is slightly reduced, the waveform dies away; oscillation ceases quite quickly. Very little change in gain is needed to effect a change from one condition to the other, and very precise control of gain is needed to maintain oscillation at constant amplitude.

The feedback elements, which may be changed manually or by some electronic control, set the frequency. The entire operation is somewhat like trying to control a weight bobbing on the end of a spring; to change its movement requires a sequence of adjustments until the new movement is achieved. Controlling a tone generator using this kind of source for music synthesis can be very cumbersome.

The other process uses a time-amplitude reference rather than a frequency-gain reference. It can take a variety of forms, but the most easily understood system generates a triangular waveform first. One way to do this is with a controlled current used to charge a capacitor until the voltage across it reached a predetermined value, then the process reverses (Fig. 6-7).

The rate of charge and discharge of the capacitor, and thus the slope of the voltage waveform, can be directly controlled. Also, the amplitude may be fixed or controlled. Both quantities are the subject of primary or direct control not, like the sinusoidal oscillator, the result of adjusting gain **until** the level is right.

With a sine-wave oscillator, a small sine wave, with the frequency controlled by the circuit elements, gradually builds up until the right level is reached. With the relaxation oscillator or function generator, it starts producing the correct amplitude and frequency, and waveform, from the beginning of the very first cycle. This makes control of its output infinitely more precise.

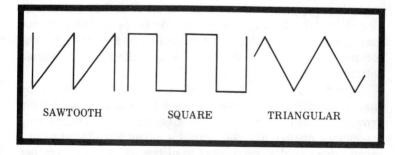

SAWTOOTH　　　　SQUARE　　　　TRIANGULAR

Fig. 6-6. These three major waveforms are produced by relaxation or function generator type oscillators.

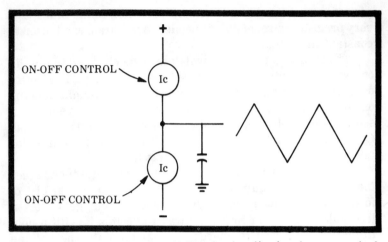

Fig. 6-7. This simple circuit illustrates the basic concept of a triangular function generator.

A relaxation oscillator can easily be made into a voltage-controlled device, so that its frequency follows any desired relationship to an input voltage. Fig. 6-8 shows a not too complicated circuit, using ordinary transistors; its frequency can be adjusted instantly by the voltage applied to the control input.

Transistor Q1 accepts the control voltage, which may vary from 1.5 to 24 volts, which in turn controls the current through the 1K resistors in its collector and emitter circuits (the resistors should be matched) from 0.9 to 23.4 milliamps, with corresponding voltages to supply plus and minus.

Transistors Q2 and Q3 are the charge and discharge controls for capacitor C; only one is operative at a time, the other being disabled by the conduction of Q4 or Q5 to reverse bias Q2 or Q3, whichever is not operating at the moment. The control currents, when Q2 or Q3 are operating, can be varied between 0.3 and 22.8 milliamps.

The points, to be determined in a minute, at which the charge direction is reversed are +6 volts and -6 volts from ground, a total change of 12 volts. Bearing in mind that 1 amp produces a change of 1 volt across a capacitor of 1 farad in 1 second, we can deduce the range of the wave period (rather than frequency; period is the basic quantity controlled here) provided.

132

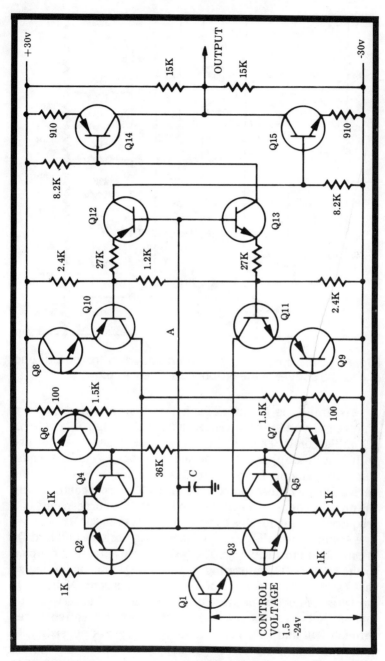

Fig. 6-8. A complete function generator circuit. For a description of its action, see the text.

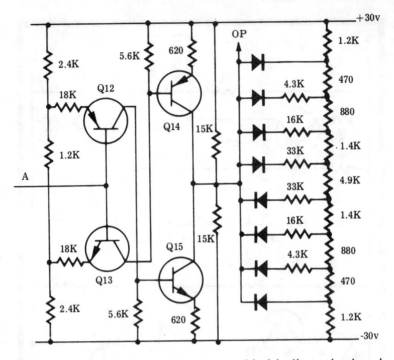

Fig. 6-9. This circuit modification added to the output end of Fig. 6-8 converts the output to a sine wave.

Assume C is 0.1 mfd. Then 1 milliamp will produce a change of 1 volt in 100 microseconds, or a change of 12 volts in 1.2 milliseconds. Thus, if the charge and discharge rates are both 1 milliamp, the full period will be 2.4 milliseconds. Currents ranging from 0.3 to 23.4 milliamps will vary the period from 8 milliseconds down to 102.5 microseconds. Using 100 microseconds as the high-speed limit, this corresponds to a frequency range, for this control, from 125 to 10,000 Hz.

Assume the voltage at "A" is moving positive and that Q5 is conducting to disable Q3. The Q5 collector current is coupled to the base of Q6, saturating it, to keep Q4 nonconducting so that Q2 maintains control of the charge current. Neither Q8 nor Q9 is conducting because the voltage at "A" is between +6 and -6 volts, values maintained at their respective bases through Q10 and Q11 from the divider network consisting of 2.4K, 1.2K and 2.4K across the supply.

As soon as the voltage at "A" reaches +6 volts, Q8 and Q10 conduct, triggering Q7 on. When Q7 turns on it disables Q5, thereby releasing Q6, so that Q4 saturates and maintains the condition, disabling Q2 and allowing Q3 to reverse the charge process.

Q12 and Q13 are follower stages, with 27K resistors between their emitters and the ultimate voltage turn-round points, and 8.2K resistors in their collectors. The voltage across the 8.2K resistors is coupled to the bases of Q14 and Q15, which have 910-ohm emitter resistors and a 15K pair in their collector circuits. This enables the output triangular waveform to be amplified, with good linearity, so it goes from +24 to -24 volts, a 48-volt swing. This can be the output of the basic "X" generator.

This triangular waveform can be made to produce a sinusoidal output of definite amplitude quite readily. However, to simplify circuitry a little, Fig. 6-9 shows an alternative output section for Fig. 6-6 that generates a sinusoidal waveform directly. Instead of the two 15K resistors in the collector load of Q14, and Q15, an additional load, con-

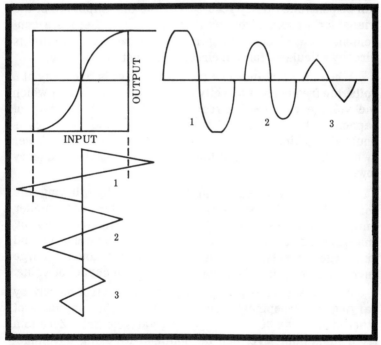

Fig. 6-10. Possible deviations from the correct waveform if the triangular waveform has the wrong magnitude: 1, too large; 2, correct; 3, too small.

135

sisting of diodes biased by the resistor chain, is added. The emitter resistors are reduced and the preceding stages changed so more current drive is available. At the center line where voltage crosses ground potential, none of the diodes are conducting, and the only collector load is the two 15K resistors.

As the output voltage goes either positive or negative, one diode after another starts conducting; thus the collector loading increases, rounding the wave into a sinusoidal. This circuit, correctly adjusted, can produce a sine wave with much less than 1 percent total harmonic content.

The shaping network produces a pure sine wave (to the degree of purity for which it is designed) at that particular amplitude only, because the function generator converts a straight line (part of the triangular wave) to a curve (quadrants of the sine wave). If the amplitude of the triangular input is wrong, only part, or too much, of the curve will be produced (Fig. 6-10).

The amplitude of a sawtooth, triangular, or square wave can be controlled fairly readily. Or, the the amplitude of the triangular wave is fixed, as it is in Fig. 6-8, there is a convenient way of controlling frequency between the limits already calculated for that circuit by adjusting the slope.

When the amplitude of a triangular wave is fixed, say at 6 volts, the frequency is directly controlled by the rate at which the voltage changes between these limits. If the rate of capacitor charge and discharge is doubled, the frequency is doubled. Making the rate of charge and discharge slower (which flattens the slope of the triangle) makes the frequency lower.

A frequency change can be effected by altering the voltage limits: the same rate of change between smaller limits raises frequency. Frequency is affected also by changing the capacitor value, keeping the same charge and discharge currents, or by changing the charge and discharge current, keeping the same voltage limits and capacitor value.

A square wave is particularly easy to control merely by varying the "chopping" point (Fig. 6-11). The amplitude of other shapes can be varied by using variable gain. Zero to a fixed maximum level can be obtained by using a voltage-variable resistance in a bridge (Fig. 6-12). Zero output is achieved when the bridge is nulled. Changing the variable element can produce an output of either phase, according to

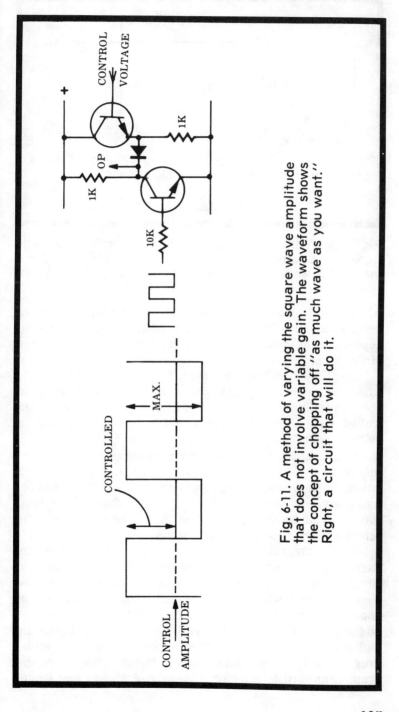

Fig. 6-11. A method of varying the square wave amplitude that does not involve variable gain. The waveform shows the concept of chopping off "as much wave as you want." Right, a circuit that will do it.

137

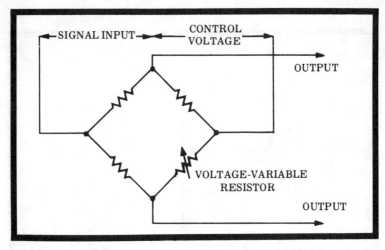

Fig. 6-12. With this bridge circuit the amplitude of any signal can be modulated by a control voltage from zero to a maximum, and even including phase reversal, if desired.

whether this element gets larger or smaller than the value needed for null. The limit to the output, in either direction, depends on the input signal and on the values in the other arms of the bridge.

Amplitude controls, whether they use variable gain or whatever, can be designed so they are voltage-controlled, as in the frequency in Fig. 6-8. Filters can also be voltage controlled. Virtually any function ingenuity can devise can now be voltage controlled.

So a complete synthesizer can be programmed to control the wave envelope of a tone, to select the starting waveform (whether sine, triangular, sawtooth or square), to control frequency, and to control filtering which changes the final content of the wave, using the basic harmonic structure of the selected waveshape as a starting point.

Using integrated circuit techniques with the elements packaged compactly, the functions can be isolated and combined with a high degree of perfection. But so far we have considered only what may be regarded as the equivalent of analog technology, the kind used in analog computers, where all the quantities are infinitely variable. Combine with this the digital techniques used in counters and synthesizers can be programmed to do many more things. They can be preprogrammed to produce a melody of almost any length with metronomic precision. Parts can be superimposed so that a complete musical ensemble will result.

A change in the envelope, the timbre, or any of the qualities can be effected with a degree of precision hitherto impossible. If anything, perhaps that is the criticism at this stage of development: the musical output is so perfect it doesn't have the character or personality that a human performer can put into it. The synthesizer's "technique" is too perfect. But, obviously, this can be modified; in fact, the possibilities are endless.

Music synthesizers can use a variety of controls. The Theremin used electrodes toward which the hands were waved like wands to control the musical effect. This type of control can be used on a synthesizer, too. However, most of the more recent innovations use one or more keyboards of conventional appearance, like organ manuals. The keyboard selects voltages that determine the frequency (pitch) or other properties of the note played. Synthesizers also can be programmed to perform any other desired function. A continuous ribbon can be used, like the one in the Martinot, as an alternative to the keyboard for any of the functions the keyboard can serve.

We have discussed one kind of tone source and modifier in which the Moog company, for one, specializes. But many other systems are possible. Moog has also demonstrated a system in which the tone source is a frequency recorded on tape. As different notes are played, a variable-speed motor, with very low inertia and feedback to accelerate precision adjustment like a servo, changes its speed fast enough to play each note the player pressed. Fig. 6-13 shows an early version of the Moog synthesizer. Fig. 6-14 pictures a typical portable arrangement of Moog modules and Fig. 6-15 is a Moog IIIp portable synthesizer. Figs. 6-16 and 6-17 show the Moog synthesizer used by Walter Carlos.

A possibility that has not yet been touched is the provision of some kind of automated synthesizer in really compact size that can be programmed by anyone, at home. One suggestion put forward specifies that the electronics for such a system be packaged in a tape cassette, instead of filling it with tape. Thus it could be plugged into any tape cassette player and you would have a midget, automated music synthesizer for the home.

Fig. 6-13. An early version of the Moog console synthesizer.

Fig. 6-14. Typical portable arrangement of the Moog modules.

Fig. 6-15. Portable Moog synthesizer.

Fig. 6-16. Synthesizer used by composer-conductor Walter Carlos.

Fig. 6-17. Walter Carlos at the console of his Moog synthesizer.

Fig. 6-18. Typical assembly of the basic ARP synthesizer.
(Courtesy Tonus, Inc.)

Fig. 6-19. Close-up showing several modules and matrix switches in the ARP system. (Courtesy Tonus, Inc.)

PUTTING A SYSTEM TOGETHER

The possibilities are almost limitless. A synthesizer system of studio quality consists of a great many units that can be patched or otherwise combined in a variety of ways. Another manufacturer, ARP, avoids patchcords altogether

146

and provides tremendous versatility of connection with a modular bus-bar system with midget slide switches. Fig. 6-18 is a front view of the basic ARP synthesizer and Fig. 6-19 is a close-up of several modules and matrix switches. The input, output, and control of each module in the system is determined by a vertical slide that connects it to any horizontal bus. Thus controls can be cascaded, waveform shapers mixed with controls, any combination you fancy can be connected in an instant by setting the slides.

Because of the complexity of such systems, whichever method of putting them together is used, a new kind of block diagram has come into existence, designed to serve electronic music composers in setting up what they want to achieve. Table 6-1 illustrates the families of symbols used, as given in a book published by Nonesuch Records (1855 Broadway, N. Y.) and issued with a 4-side (12-inch, 33 RPM LP) demonstration series, number HC-73018, that gives a uniquely devised demonstration of the various kinds of effects available, as conceived and put together by Paul Beaver and Bernard Krause.

To use these symbols, a standard block diagram layout is used: symbols that represent initiating signals are placed at the upper left, with outputs from the system to the upper right. Signal inputs enter a symbol at its left and leave at its right. Control voltages enter the symbol at the bottom and leave the device generating the control at its top. Letters, possibly with numbers as well, indicate the kind of function a symbol performs or generates within the class indicated by the shape of the symbol.

A sine-wave generator has only one waveform but can be varied in frequency. So a transient generator operating as a voltage control will change the frequency of a sine-wave generator at the beginning of its voice, settling to a steady pitch, unless it is programmed to do something else, like warble.

On the other hand, a sawtooth generator operates in either phase: that is, it can ascend slowly, with a sudden drop, or descend slowly, with a sudden rise. As a signal generator, the choice does not affect the sound in any noticeable way, but where a sawtooth generator is used as a voltage control, usually at a much lower (subaudio) frequency, the difference between the two can be very marked.

147

TABLE 6-1.

TABLE OF DIAGRAMMATIC SYMBOLS

Periodic and/or continuous source

(S) Sine wave generator

(N) Sawtooth wave generator

(L) Rectangular wave generator, assumed to be square wave unless the "L" is followed by a number other than 2. The appended number indicates both the elimination of harmonics divisible by it and the denominator of the fraction of the period of the duty cycle.

(V) Triangular wave generator

(G) Graphical waveform synthesizer

(W) White sound generator

(P) Pink sound generator

Nonperiodic and/or triggered source

⟨P⟩ Programmed sequential pulse generator

⟨T⟩ Transient generator

Frequency and/or phase modulator

◇R◇ Ring modulator

◇F◇ Frequency shifter (Klangumwandler)

◇P◇ Phase modulator

Frequency divider; assumed divisor is 2 unless the "D" is followed by another number.

 Frequency multiplier; assumed multiplier is 2 unless the "M" is followed by another number.

 Time base or tempo shifter

Filter, assumed to be band pass unless otherwise designated

 High pass filter

 Low pass filter

 Band reject or notch filter

Amplifier

 Gating amplifier, assumed linear response unless the "G" is followed by a number designating order of exponential function.

 Volume expander

Attenuator or pad

 Volume compressor

 Volume limiter

Redundancy multiplier

 Reverberation generator

 Echo generator, single repeat

△X△ Attack multiplier or repeater, multiple echo generator

△C△ Clipper

△D△ Distorter

External signal source

⌐) Acoustic input transducer or microphone

(| Acoustic output transducer

⌐⌐ Mechanical input transducer or vibration pickup

⌐⌐ Mechanical output transducer or vibrator

⌐) Magnetic input transducer (tape playback)

(Magnetic output transducer (tape recorder)

[ ]

Control transducer

| F | Frequency follower

| E | Envelope amplitude follower

| T | Time delay

| S | Switch

| K | Keyboard, multiple switch, or discrete positional pressure control

| C | Capacitance or proximity control

| P | Continuous positional control, assumed to be in one dimension (linear or ribbon control) unless the "P" is followed by either a "2" (planar or pantograph control) or a "3" (spatial control)

| D | Digital follower (digital-to-analog interface)

For example, if a sawtooth generator is used to control frequency, the signal output will be either a rising or a falling tone with a quick return, repeating its action at the rate determined by the control sawtooth frequency. Again, if a sawtooth is applied to a voltage-controlled amplifier to vary gain, the pitch will not vary but the intensity will in a similar manner, either rising to a maximum and starting over or starting at maximum and falling to a minimum, with an effect like a rather synthetic bell. These effects are very distinctive.

The rectangular-wave generator is understood to be a square wave, unless a numeral is used to indicate a duty cycle other than 2. For example, a generator designated L3 will have a cycle in which one horizontal section has twice the time duration of the other.

As has been stated before, a square wave contains only odd harmonics. But when the duty cycle, or up-down ratio, is changed from the balanced square wave, the content of the wave changes. Fig. 6-20 shows the frequency content of waves of various proportions. Along the top, the scale gives the L numbers by which the wave would be identified on the music synthesizer code for rectangular waves. At the bottom, the shorter part of the wave is expressed as a fraction of the whole period. (The bottom scale is the reciprocal of the L numbers along the top.) And nulls in frequency are also identified along the bottom.

Notice that an L3 wave nulls the third, sixth, and ninth harmonics, just as an L2 wave (the balanced sqaure wave) nulls all even harmonics, while an L4 wave nulls the fourth and eighth. The shorter the pulse, which means the higher the L number, the more reedy the tone sounds. One form of modulation applicable, but so far little used, is to voltage-control the duty cycle of a tone in which the frequency is fixed or independently controlled.

The vertical scale in Fig. 6-20 uses the amplitude of the fundamental as 1 and expresses amplitude of various harmonics as fractions of this amplitude. The amplitude of the rectangular wave producing the syntheses is not shown, but it gets bigger to achieve the same amplitude of the fundamental as the wave becomes more asymmetrical (toward the left of the chart).

The triangular wave generator is normally symmetrical, but it need not be. Mathematically and by electronic derivation,

151

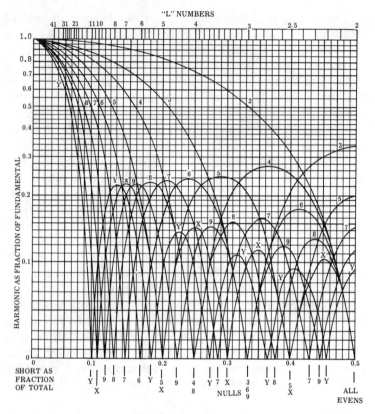

Fig. 6-20. Chart showing how the frequency composition varies as the proportions of a rectangular wave are changed.

it can be the integral of a rectangular wave. So the up can be steeper and shorter than the down, or vice versa (Fig. 6-21). Introducing this concept relates all the waveforms together, because a sawtooth is now a special form of triangular in which the up or the down has become infinitely steep (or very nearly so).

A graphical waveform synthesizer can produce any other desired waveform by graphical synthesis, just as a sine wave can be derived from a triangular. It merely requires that different control constants be fed into the system to make some other shape. Another possibility is the generation of a wave directly from a drawn or otherwise physically generated waveshape by some form of transducer action.

152

A few electronic organs use mechanically-driven tone wheels, like the Hammond, but with complete waveforms engraved for electrical instead of magnetic pickup, rather than a relatively pure sine wave which the Hammond uses.

In addition to this family of periodic generators, each of which has some specific frequency or waveform content, are the aperiodic generators, producing white or colored sound (noisè). White noise, like white light, consists of a mixture of frequencies uniformly distributed but of random intensity. Without modification it sounds like hiss or a rushing sound.

White noise can be colored by passing it through filters, in which case it may take on the character of specific notes if the bandpass is narrow, or it may become a colored sound when a broader filter is used. Filters can be voltage controlled for both frequency and bandwidth, providing a wide range of possible effects.

The hexagonal symbol (Table 6-1) represents a variety of generators used exclusively for control voltages. Any of the other generator forms can work, either at frequencies in the audio range or below it (slower) to provide control voltages that modify other signals, in one of the many ways possible, as well as providing a signal source in themselves.

The programmed sequential pulse generator can be, for example, a counter, programmed to provide sequential

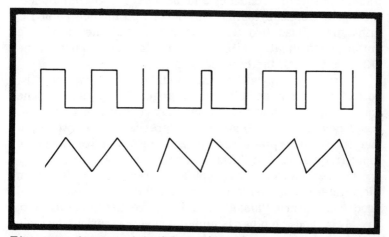

Fig. 6-21. Asymmetric triangular waves and corresponding asymmetric rectangular waves.

153

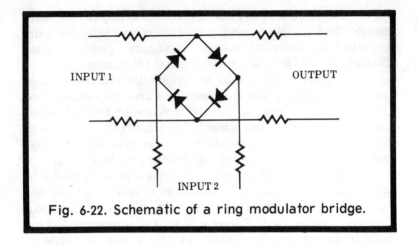

Fig. 6-22. Schematic of a ring modulator bridge.

voltages that will play a tune automatically and set up specific chords or arpeggios. The transient generator shapes the amplitude or frequency contour of each note played, according to previously prescribed requirements.

The nest group of symbols, diamond shape, stand for signal modifiers, other than simple gain or frequency changes. The ring modulator (Fig. 6-22) takes two inputs and literally multiplies their waveforms together. Thus, if either input is zero, there is no output, because zero times anything is zero (a mathematical as well as physical fact). If one input is a signal of specific frequency and the other is a DC imbalance, the signal frequency output will depend on the degree of DC imbalance. Used this way, the device becomes a simple amplitude modulator, with a provision to reverse phase if the DC goes through the balance point.

More often, though, a ring modulator uses two signals, both of which may be in the audio range. Multiplying two sine waves together yields an output that contains neither input frequency, only the sum and difference of the two input frequencies. This produces an interesting sound, related to the input frequencies but different from either of them.

If other than sine-wave inputs are used, the result is even more interesting. Using two frequencies in the audio band produces a form of "klang" tone. If one frequency is subaudio, say, 6 Hz, and the other is audio, it yields a curious tremolo that includes phase reversal, somewhat like the phantom effect described earlier.

154

The frequency shifter is a highly complex device that performs a function relative to frequency, while the ring modulator's performance multiplies waveform amplitudes. The frequency shifter is an extremely sophisticated device and thus beyond the reach of any but the wealthiest experimenters. Also, many very similar effects can be obtained with far less expensive equipment units.

The phase modulator is used to shift the phase of the input signal in accordance with a voltage control; thus it can serve to create vibrato effects after the signal has been generated as a steady tone, although the vibrato effect that this device can create is somewhat limited (frequency control of the generator is simpler and more effective). But a phase modulator can be used to create choir effects; shifting phase at appropriate speeds can, when outputs differently shifted are combined, produce an interesting choral effect, as if there are several voices instead of only one (Fig. 6-23).

Frequency dividers are simple, like those used in organs. They usually just drop the tone by exactly an octave. If a number other than 2 follows the D, a different frequency division occurs.

Frequency multipliers are slightly more complex than dividers but serve a function precisely the opposite. Essentially, they consist of generators, dividers, comparators and

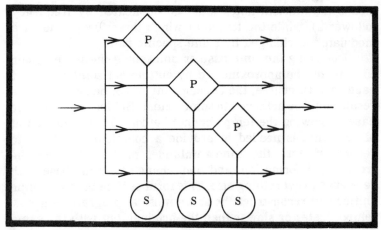

Fig. 6-23. This diagram shows a method of providing multiple phase modulation to achieve a choral effect. (See Table 6-1 for symbol designations.)

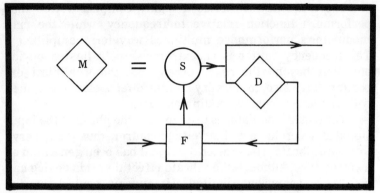

Fig. 6-24. Diagram illustrating the composition of a frequency multiplier in terms of simpler units.

feedback, so the generator is adjusted to produce two cycles of output for every cycle of input (Fig. 6-24).

A time base or tempo shifter is again a generic term and can represent a variety of devices. However, it should be noted that changing speed is not the same as changing time base or tempo. When speed is changed, as by varying the speed control of a recorder or record player, both pitch and tempo change together. Doubling the speed makes a given piece of music play in half the time at an octave higher pitch.

Changing time base or tempo without changing pitch means the musical notes must be duplicated by frequency follower(s), while the tempo at which these frequencies are modulated is changed by some specific ratio.

Shortening the time base or quickening the tempo could conceivably be approximated by cutting out some cycles of each note. Of course, the envelope might not be right, but the result would be achieved to some extent. But lengthening time base or slowing the tempo cannot be done by this method at all. So what is needed to provide a complete facility is to record or store the time-amplitude, modulation, and the frequency information, and then change the time base with reference to everything else. This form of time base or tempo shifter will reconstruct the same musical program to a new tempo, faster or slower than the original, but with the same pitch.

The symbols for filters should be self-explanatory, as are those for amplifier, attenuator, and redundancy multipliers;

the latter is an interesting term borrowed from computer technology. All the properties and functions listed under this heading duplicate "information" already present, musically. A reverberation generator compounds the signal with a somewhat confused multiple echo. An echo generator provides just one specific echo, similar to that supplied by a tape delay unit.

The attack multiplier or repeater, or multiple echo generator, makes the sound keep repeating itself, according to the programmed attack form. Clippers and other distorters add more information or frequencies to the sound already present, but related to it. The effect is like the sound teenagers like so much, treated earlier as "fuzz."

Symbols for a means of introducing or providing external signal interfaces are self-explanatory, although if you were to encounter a schematic that used them without this definition, you would wonder what they signified.

Control transducers, square symbols, use the standard connections described earlier. A control input is applied from the bottom and a control output appears at the top, a signal input from the left and a signal output to the right.

With the variety of equipment represented by the symbols in Table 6-1, an enormous range of possibilities is presented; we've merely scratched the surface so far. In addition to what can be done in an individual channel, similar controls can vary

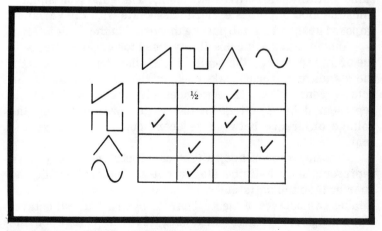

Fig. 6-25. Chart showing the possible direct transformations of the four basic waveforms.

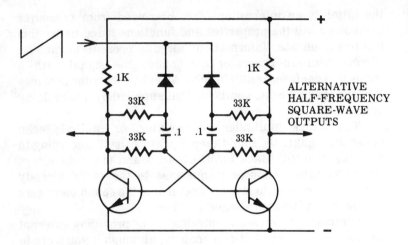

Fig. 6-26. This circuit converts a sawtooth wave to a square wave of half the frequency. Each vertical excursion of the sawtooth coincides with one vertical of the square wave.

distribution between two or more stereo tracks, producing even more solid effects.

On the demonstration records referred to earlier (Nonesuch HC-73018) some very self-descriptive sounds have been transcribed, illustrating the fact that different shapes have a dual and sometimes even a triple significance. Waveform and change in intensity and frequency all follow the same pattern: sine-wave, sawtooth, triangular, or square. Thus the kind of tone is easier to associate with the variation imposed upon it. It is like putting the visual in the audio!

Another interesting possibility, used for various effects, is the ability to change the scale of this kind of instrument. On the standard musical scale used in the Western world, an octave consists of 12 semitones. As each of these is represented by a voltage in the synthesizer, changing the voltage difference between adjacent notes can change the scale.

Choosing the voltage so that each note on the keyboard represents only half the standard tone interval yields the quarter-tone tuning (standard is semitone, remember). Thus it takes two octaves of the keyboard to span a musical octave. Expanding the voltage difference, so one octave of the keyboard produces enough voltage for four musical octaves makes each note interval two tones, called a ditone scale.

Two factors are important in achieving a scale change: (1) the voltage control of frequency must be precisely logarithmic so that the interval in voltage for each semitone change in frequency, or each octave, or any specific musical interval, is the same at all parts of the musical scale; and the condensation of voltage must be strictly proportionate so that half the voltage for an octave represents half an octave.

To clarify what can be done, the table in Fig. 6-25 shows the changes in waveform that can be achieved by simple circuit transformation. Of course, any waveform can be changed into any other, but not all of them directly. And some forms of synthesis are possible, using more than one of a wave to produce one of another. For example, a sawtooth can be synthesized from an infinite range of octave-related square waves, or a sqaure wave can be synthesized by combining a pair of octave related sawtooth waves. Fig. 6-25 does not include such synthesis, merely direct transformation from one waveform to another.

A sawtooth can be converted to a square wave of half frequency by using it to trigger a bistable multivibrator (Fig. 6-26). Or it can be converted into a triangular waveform by centering it against the supply voltage, producing a constant-voltage source by means of an emitter follower. Then a phase splitter inverts the bottom half of the sawtooth (below half

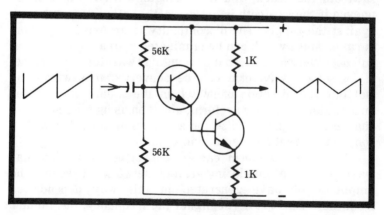

Fig. 6-27. A circuit for converting a sawtooth to a triangular wave of the same frequency and half the amplitude. The vertical spike on the output wave, coincident with the sawtooth "flyback," can easily be eliminated with a small capacitor.

159

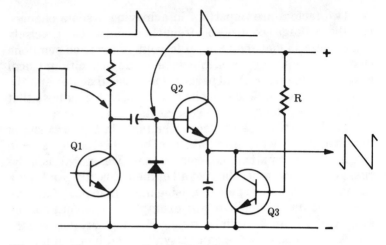

Fig. 6-28. A more refined circuit for converting a square wave to a sawtooth. Q1 is one of the sqaure-wave generator transistors. Q2 charges the sawtooth-generating capacitor and Q3 provides the constant-current discharge controlled by R.

supply voltage) and during the top half interval the transistor just becomes a direct transfer conductor (Fig. 6-27).

There is a discontinuity in the new waveform where the sawtooth flies back, and the triangular wave will also be uneven if the sawtooth is not correctly balanced in DC level against the supply. The discontinuity is an extremely short duration spike which can be eliminated with a capacitor that will not otherwise disturb the triangular waveform otherwise.

A square waveform can be converted to sawtooth by isolating the direction of switch in the square wave, after differentiation of the waveform, and then using the result as a charge or discharge pulse for a capacitor provided with a constant current reverse action (Fig. 6-28).

A square waveform can be converted to a triangular waveform by a simple integrating network. However, the amplitude of wave generated in this way depends on frequency (Fig. 6-29). The higher the frequency, the smaller the output triangular wave, unless the integrating time constant is changed. One possibility here is to use voltage control on the square-wave amplitude, and then use a signal derived from the triangular wave output, possibly with delay, to control the amplitude of the square wave (Fig. 6-30).

160

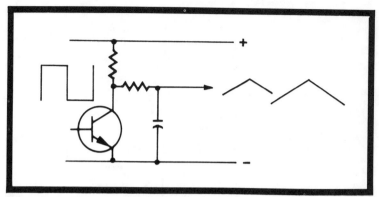

Fig. 6-29. This simple circuit converts a square wave to a triangular. Notice that the lower the frequency (longer period) of the input the larger the amplitude of the output when the same R and C values are used.

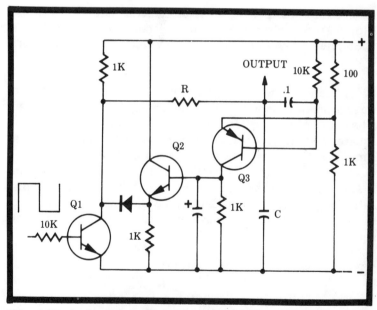

Fig. 6-30. A circuit designed to control the amplitude of the triangular wave output: Q1 amplifies the square; Q2 limits it (Q2 is controlled by Q3). With the values shown the triangular waveform output will be one-tenth the supply voltage, provided that integrating components R and C allow the amplitude to reach the supply level with an unlimited square-wave input.

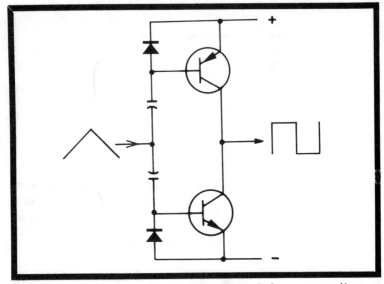

Fig. 6-31. A relatively simple circuit for converting a triangular wave to square wave. Values of the capacitors are chosen to suit the slope of the triangular wave input.

A triangular wave can readily be converted to a square wave by using a slope sensor on the triangular wave to trigger alternate conducting transistors on and off to produce the square wave (Fig. 6-31). Converting a triangular wave to a sinusoidal has already been discussed quite fully.

The only kind of wave that can readily be generated from a sine wave is a square wave, and it is done by simply saturating a stage or two. Each stage clips off more and more of the tops of the sine wave until the desired degree of squareness is achieved.

FUNCTIONS OF PROGRAMMING

The addition of programming to synthetic music has added not one but a whole host of new dimensions. In the simplest sense, using one waveform generator to control the envelope, tone structure, or any other property of the main tone generator is a form of programming and, as it involves a form of contour or shape it would be called a simple "analog" programmer (as opposed to the digital possibility). But the concept of advance programming of what one or more tones will do, when initiated as a sequence or other type program by the composer, introduces a virtually infinite range of possibilities never before thought of. In a sense the early RCA synthesizer used a form of digital programming: punched paper tape. This method is being used today with many different adaptations.

One possibility of such use is illustrated at Fig. 6-32. It uses a punched tape with eight hole positions. The first four determine the pitch within an octave, while two more determine a 4-octave range with four extra notes on the top octave, if desired, making a total range of 52 notes. This uses only six of the eight holes. The remaining two can serve an "address" function. One combination can identify the six already designated as the generator pitch selection, a second can determine the envelope, while a third can determine a filter selection. For the filter selection, two specifications are needed: center frequency and width. So the first four could pick the frequency while the remaining two select four degrees of filter width.

Now, to use such a program; first the "A" address is used to select a note to be played, this information will be stored into the synthesizer's "memory." Next the "B" address is used to pick a filter frequency and width that will control the tone quality when the note plays. Finally, the "C" address is used to trigger the envelope required.

This last function has four envelop generators that can be used separately or in combination, since voltages control the envelope and voltages may be added. Also, there are two more squelch effects to terminate the note, either by expediting the decay at a given point or by acting more suddenly, like a damper.

To play a note with this sequencer, after the tone has been initiated by the envelope trigger, further instructions from the coder can change its quality as it decays by changing the filtering used, or it can produce a glissando effect by changing the pitch. Here again, further modifiers can be fed in to determine whether pitch changes instantly, as by frets on a guitar, or at a desired glissando rate by controlling the pitch voltage change rate.

The above technique is one method of control. Preparing the paper tape may be time consuming, but the equipment and supplies to operate it are relatively inexpensive and it does

163

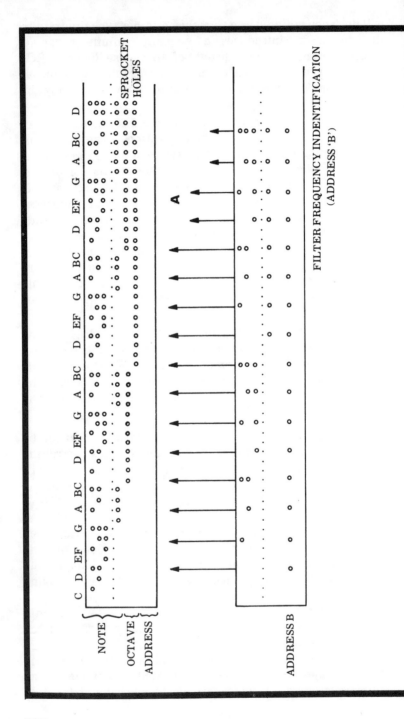

C D EF G A BC D EF G A BC D EF G A BC D EF G A BC D

SPROCKET HOLES

NOTE
OCTAVE
ADDRESS

A

FILTER FREQUENCY INDENTIFICATION
(ADDRESS 'B')

ADDRESS B

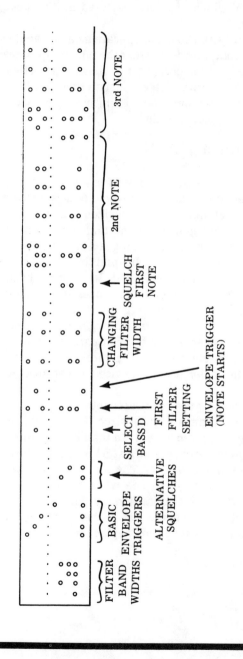

Fig. 6-32. A typical punch coding system used to program a synthesizer. The "combinations" shown are just some possibilities, leaving open places for additions, not actual system diagrams.

have considerable versatility. An electronic sequencer is another way, some possibilities of which we have discussed already and some of which are demonstrated in the package referred to earlier.

Greater versatility and speed of operation can be achieved by programming a computer to do what the punch tape does in only a limited way. Then the computer "follows instructions," which can get quite complicated (instructions within instructions with instructions ad infinitum), controlling everything the synthesizer can do.

SERVICING SYNTHESIZERS

Any large size synthesizer consists of many units that can be patched together to produce whatever effect is desired at the moment. Thus each unit can be serviced separately, and the patch cords can be repaired in the manner patch cords always have been, of course. Servicing a sophisticated unit such as those used in synthesizers is beyond this book, because of the great variety of circuits involved. In general, because many precision units are included, it reduces to a matter of finding the defective one and replacing the whole unit.

Probably, like servicing electronic organs, synthesizers are apt to scare a serviceman by their apparent complexity. Yet really, in modern electronics, the more complicated a system becomes, the easier it is to service. It just **looks** more complicated!

In comparison an organ is integrated into a single entity to a much greater extent than is a synthesizer. Thus fault tracing in an organ is likely to be more involved than in a synthesizer. Because of the greater degree of unitization in the synthesizer, localizing a fault is much easier. The various units can be patched up in different ways to see what works and what doesn't, and the faulty unit identified by relatively simple deduction. The technician should not bother too much with "fixing" a faulty unit. Just send for a replacement.

Chapter 7

Troubleshooting

With the preceding chapters as a background, it is appropriate to consider troubleshooting and repair in greater detail. Eventually, any electronic gear needs repair, and electronic musical instruments are certainly no exception. Whether you're a professional technician or a musician with a yen to dig into the electronics, it is hoped the following will help.

TRADITIONAL INSTRUMENTS

If the instrument is dead, work back from the output (the loudspeaker) to establish that each part is working, until you come to the unit or stage containing the fault. Is the loudspeaker working? When the amplifier is switched on, listen closely to the loudspeaker diaphragm for a slight hum, evidence that the amplifier is on. If you can hear it and are sure the hum is coming from the loudspeaker diaphragm, then you can safely assume that the loudspeaker and some part of the amplifier must be working.

However, if you can hear no hum or hiss at all, the fault could be either with the loudspeaker or in the amplifier. You could check the DC supply voltage in the amplifier as a way of determining that you at least have supply. If there is no DC supply, either the output transistors or the loudspeaker could be faulty.

Check the loudspeaker with the amplifier switched off by applying an ohmmeter across the voice coil. You should get a resistance reading on the meter. If the amplifier has an output transformer, it will almost short-circuit the loudspeaker voice coil to DC, so it would be well to disconnect the loudspeaker and apply the resistance measurement to just the voice coil side of the connection (Fig. 7-1). In addition to the continuity indication you should be able to hear a click or plop from the loudspeaker diaphragm as the ohmmeter connection is made

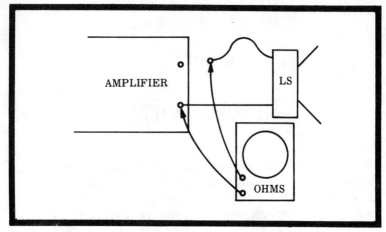

Fig. 7-1. The first thing to check in a dead amplifier system is the loudspeaker.

and broken. If you get a resistance reading but hear nothing, the voice coil must be jammed somehow so it cannot move, unless it happens to be totally short-circuited, which is unlikely.

Having ascertained that the loudspeaker is working, move back to see whether the amplifier output stage is working. First, it needs a DC supply, so check that, if you have not done so already. Make sure that the DC is reaching the transistors.

If the output stage has protection circuits, check them to see that they have not permanently shorted the output stage drive, which can happen. Such a condition can be deduced only by careful voltage measurement between the output transistor base and emitter or from the drive transistor base to the output (Fig. 7-2). The voltage measured here should be the contact potential of the transistors involved, about 0.6 volt for each (silicon) transistor. If it is appreciably less than this, or even zero, a protection transistor probably is shorting out the drive.

If one or both output transistors have blown, they will read open with an ohmmeter. On the other hand, an output transistor can become a short circuit, in which case a fuse will usually blow. If you have a blown fuse in a solid-state circuit, one method of checking is to use an external DC supply instead of the one built into the amplifier, with a protective resistance in series that will allow full quiescent voltage to appear if the

168

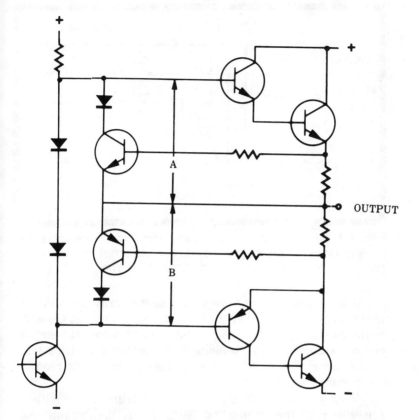

Fig. 7-2. Circuit protective features can kill the output stage. Voltages measured at A and B should be small but measurable, according to the contact potential of the transistors involved. Any variation will indicate the nature of the fault in the protective circuit.

transistors are OK, but prevent damage to the supply if they are shorted (Fig. 7-3).

An advantage of this technique is that transistors can be removed, one by one, until the short disappears, as indicated by the restoration of normal voltages. The use of an external supply eliminates the need to continually replace fuses and the temptation to bypass the fuse during troubleshooting. Once the defective transistor is found and replaced, you can check the circuit with the controlled supply before returning the amplifier to its own.

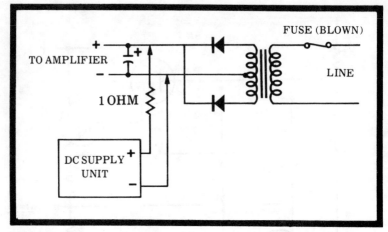

Fig. 7-3. When a fuse has blown, you avoid unnecessary repeat performances by using an external test supply (with protective resistor) until you find the short.

It is a good rule not to replace a blown transistor without conducting a fairly thorough check to find out why it blew. A protection circuit may have gone bad, in which case the output circuit is unprotected. Replacing the output transistor will restore the circuit so it functions, but it will blow quite readily when subjected to an overload.

Most troubles with conventional instrument amplifiers are either in the connecting leads or in the pickup and microphone fixtures. Periodically microphones or pickups go bad and need replacing. In some instruments, such as an accordian, you must check for phasing when replacing a microphone. If you replace only one microphone, it may not be wired the same as the others, so check phasing by playing the chromatic scale to see that all notes play with equal loudness over the loudspeaker system.

If a microphone is not identical in type with the one it replaces, its sensitivity may be different. If the new one is more sensitive, this discrepancy can be corrected by inserting a resistance in series if the units are connected in parallel or in parallel if the units are connected in series (Fig. 7-4). With parallel connected ceramic microphones a capacitor may prove a better way of cutting down the oversensitive mike, but finding the right value capacitor will be a matter of trial and error.

170

On stringed instruments, particularly a guitar, correct adjustment of the pickup(s) in relation to the strings is important. If the space between the strings and the top of the pickup is too great, the pickup will be insensitive. If it is too small, the strings may actually strike the pickup and buzz. The pickups should be mounted so they come as close to the strings as possible without any liabliity for the strings to touch the pickup, however vigorously they are plucked.

A bass mike should give little trouble, but its frequency response may affect the sound of the instrument. The instrument maker, if he installed the mike, probably picked one to give an acceptable bass quality. If you can, get an exact replacement. If not, you may have to try to fix the sound, by using a shunt capacitor to eliminate unwanted high peaks, for example. If the response contains peaks (as is the case with

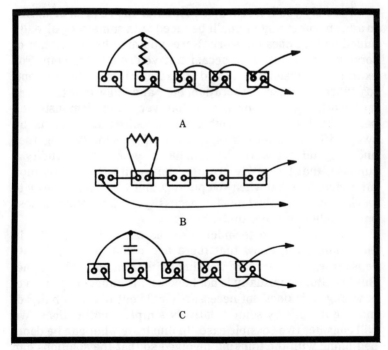

Fig. 7-4. If a replacement microphone in a multiple-unit pickup is too sensitive the drawings show several ways to equalize it: (A), for dynamics, parallel connected; (B), for dynamics, series connected; (C), for ceramics, parallel connected.

171

some inexpensive mikes) where they are not wanted, they cannot easily be removed by additional circuit components. A very complicated multichannel filter might correct it, but getting a mike better suited for the job would be far less expensive (and less bulky) than that solution.

The so-called electronic piano is a relatively simple instrument. If a reed or pickup becomes defective, the best thing to do is to replace it. And the only place you will find such a replacement is from the manufacturer; it is not that common an instrument.

You may also need to make corrections if the microphone or pickup is not suited to the amplifier to which it is connected. That problem is treated in the relevant chapters.

ADDITION OF ELECTRONIC MODIFIERS

Possibly you'll frequently encounter the request or desire to add on something or you'll be faced with something already added on that does not work. Here, you may be the victim of some misinformation on occasion if you're a technician. For example, a musician may add an extra unit to his instrument, say vibrato, fuzz, reverberation, etc., and know that the extra unit works because he heard that very unit demonstrated before he bought it (or otherwise acquired it, such as by swap). His amplifier works, so when he puts the two together and they do not work, he concludes, with some validity I suppose, that his newly acquired unit quit! It is a common misconception that when you put together two things known to work separately, they must of necessity work together, unless one or other of them quits.

Of course, as a technician or, as one knowledgeable in electronics, you know that there are technically legitimate reasons why two or more working units fail to operate as one. But the situation usually is not hopeless. If impedance or level is wrong, this does not necessarily rule out the possibility of making it work by some relatively simple modifications. We will consider two possible cases to illustrate what can be done, beginning with the thinking involved so that the solutions can be applied to a wider variety of situations by appropriately adjusted thinking.

First, suppose a device that is to be inserted has virtually zero gain (same output level as input level) to provide vibrato, fuzz, echo, etc. The effect to be provided is unimportant for our consideration here, since the method of determining what needs changing is the same whichever kind of unit it is. Suppose the amplifier connections are designed for low-impedance say, 50 ohms, but the device to be inserted is intended to work at high impedances of the order of 100,000 ohms, in and out (Fig. 7-5).

Connecting a 50-ohm source to an input designed for 100,000 ohms will not usually cause any difficulty, except that the resulting voltage level will be much lower. For the same nominal power level (dbm) this change in impedance represents a level drop of 33 db, unless steps are taken to convert the power. At the output of the device, however, connecting a circuit designed for 100,000 ohms to an input designed for 50 ohms can cause trouble. If the coupling capacitor is intended to feed a 100K load, a 50-ohm load could cause a serious loss of bass and an intolerable drop in the voltage level.

First, the job requires an "up" match, a transistor to provide about 33 db gain, with an input of 50 ohms. That is a voltage gain of about 50 (34 db would be 50). A transistor with a collector resistor of 1000 ohms and a base resistor of 20 ohms (use an 18-ohm resistor) will give the requisite voltage gain (Fig. 7-6). If the transistor has a beta of 100, its base input resistance will be about 1.8K, so you'll need to load it with 56

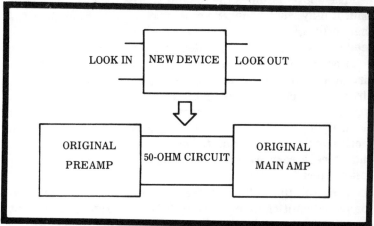

Fig. 7-5. This mismatch problem illustrates a typical situation which can occur when you attempt to integrate an auxiliary unit.

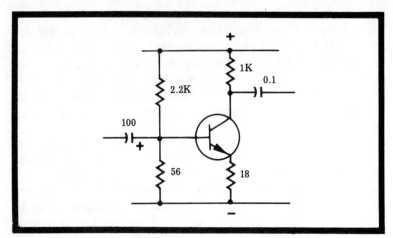

Fig. 7-6. A matching circuit to convert from 50 to 100K with appropriate level correction.

ohms to get an input that looks like 50 ohms. Now, to get half the supply voltage at the collector, the emitter should have about one-fortieth the supply voltage because the resistor there is one-twentieth the collector resistor. So, assuming a germanium transistor (if a silicon is used, a different value will be required) the upper part of a bias potentiometer will need to be about 40 times 56 ohms, or 2.2K.

The above assumes the 50-ohm source "wants" a 50-ohm load. It may want a higher value, such as 250 ohms. Just exchange the 56-ohm and 2.2K resistors for 270 and 10K or as needed to get the correct collector operating voltage.

For coupling capacitors, 100 mfd will serve for the 50-ohm circuit and 0.1 mfd for the 100K circuit. Suitable values may already be included in the unit between which the impedance-changer level-matcher is connected. However, watch that any electrolytics are correctly polarized. Find which side gets the more positive voltage due to the respective circuit supplies and, if necessary, reverse the connection to ensure correct polarization.

Now for the output of the new device. A Darlington-connected emitter follower (Fig. 7-7) will protect the output circuit from being loaded down by the 50-ohm input. At the Darlington output add another 56-ohm resistor in series, with a suitable coupling capacitor to operate at 50 to 100 ohms (say 50 or 100 mfd) and a 100-ohm emitter resistor. Bias resistors of 330K each will keep the input impedance high.

The coupling capacitor internal to the unit will serve here. The only loss will be about 6 db, due to the division between the external 56-ohm resistor and the original 50-ohm input. As you have already provided 33 db gain at the input end, you may actually need a loss at the output to enable the levels to work together.

Putting another 56-ohm resistor across the input will ensure correct termination of the following unit. Now the combination looks like about 25 ohms. To lose the 33 db you gained with the impedance change, a resistor of 40 to 50 times 25 ohms should go in series: 1,000 ohms. Now using a single emitter follower with 1000 ohms as its load and a large capacitor to couple from the 56-ohm part (Fig. 7-8), the matching is again readily achieved for both level and impedance.

Now let's reverse the situation: suppose the original connections are high-impedance types but the newly acquired device has a low-impedance input and output. The procedure is simply reversed, and if you reason the whole thing through, the same things apply: level and impedance changes fit the needs (Fig. 7-9). In either circuit, if the supply is of the opposite polarity, use opposite polarity transistors, and correspondingly change the connections of the electrolytics.

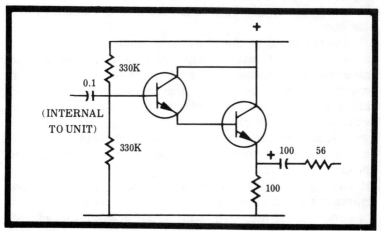

Fig. 7-7. A high-to-low impedance (100K to 50 ohms) matching circuit.

175

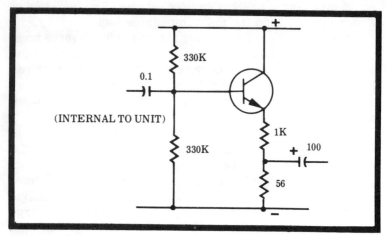

Fig. 7-8. This circuit provides a better match and gain level between a high and low impedance.

Obtaining a supply for these extra stages should not be difficult; one unit or the other probably will be capable of handling the additional drain, since the requirements of the extra stages are low. However, finding somewhere to mount the extra stages may not be quite so easy. If the level at which they operate is low, they will need to be encased in suitable shielded boxes or else built inside the unit to which they are attached.

Another problem that may occur with so-called electric instruments is the use of amplifier equipment common to more than one instrument. The alternative is to use separate amplifier and speaker combinations for every instrument and this is often done. It has advantages, because intermodulation between the instruments is avoided.

It is not uncommon these days for fairly small groups to have an aggregate audio power of 1,000 watts or more, a power the listeners feel rather than hear, but that's the way they like it! The high modulation in the small space probably causes considerable intermodulation in the air around the performers, even if the equipment is "pure." But who cares? However, pushing all those sounds through a single 1,000-watt (or higher) amplifier and then into a massive loudspeaker system could easily cause much more trouble.

If such a group is concerned with economy, for packaging or travel purposes, a common amplification system is the logical answer. Probably the best way is to get a mixer and ensure that everything matches correctly (Fig. 7-10).

Now you need to be sure that each instrument feed matches the mixer and that the mixer matches the amplifier. If there is any mismatch, you will need to take steps similar to those just discussed to achieve matching. Beyond this, some good hints appear at the end of Chapter 3.

FULLY ELECTRONIC INSTRUMENTS

Fully electronic instruments, such as the Theremin (very rare now), Martenot, Ondioline, are usually built in the traditional way prevalent before integrated circuits and other prepackaged units made the scene. They incorporate some mechanical controls, such as a keyboard, slidewire control, etc., all of which may need service.

The first thing in any such instance is to thoroughly digest the schematic, particularly the part or parts that may be suspected of being faulty for whatever reason. Also, there may be a manual that gives more information, such as a description of the principle of operation; all such information is valuable. But most instruments of this type were built by people who preferred secrecy, probably as a protection against being copied, and either did most of the work themselves or trained people personally for the job.

This means that adequate information will be difficult to come by. Schematics may not be updated from earlier models to later ones, so that even if you acquire a schematic it may not be correct for the model in front of you. In cases where there's little to go on it is best to contact the manufacturer for help, which is what the manufacturer wanted, presumably.

SYNTHESIZERS

Synthesizer troubleshooting is a different picture altogether. Manufacturers of synthesizers are doing a booming business; this is the latest trend in music and they have all the business they can handle. They are also planning expansion into markets never reached by the earlier electronic instruments: schools, home entertainment, etc.

177

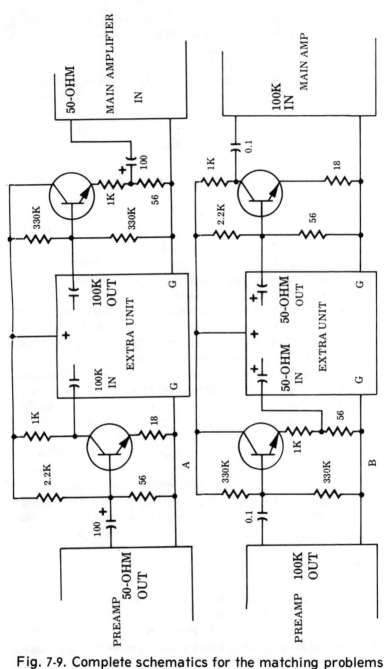

Fig. 7-9. Complete schematics for the matching problems discussed.

You will find them more cooperative than their earlier counterparts in supplying service data. However, practical limitations, because they use so much integrated circuitry and prepackaged units, makes it almost essential to work on a replacement rather than a "fix-it" basis.

So, as suggested earlier, your problem reduces to that of finding the faulty unit and getting a replacement for it. If a connection is faulty, it is possible you can fix it, if the connection is a simple one. However, if it is a multiway connector, "fixing" may be no more feasible here than in the units themselves. The best way may again be to obtain a replacement connector.

Power supplies are not as prefabricated and use fewer (if any) ICs than the rest of the circuit. So you may find a need to repair a regulated supply, a process that follows more conventional procedure. When a regulated voltage goes bad, there may be no voltage at all or it may just lose its regulation so the voltage level is not reliable.

Most regulated voltages are referenced to one or more zener diodes. Such a diode may fail, which usually means it blows, due to excessive current. This means the voltage across it will usually rise because the current through it ceases.

On the other hand, a zener diode may lose its regulation characteristic. This may happen due to an overload that does

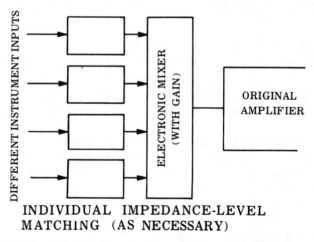

INDIVIDUAL IMPEDANCE-LEVEL
MATCHING (AS NECESSARY)

Fig. 7-10. An electronic mixer may be used to feed several instruments into a single amplifier system. Correct matching is necessary in each case.

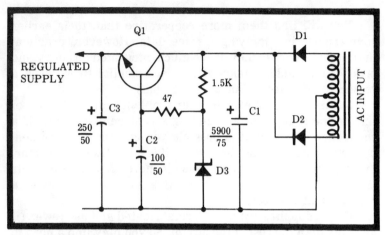

Fig. 7-11. A simpler voltage regulator circuit.

not quite blow it. A very firmly regulated supply is essential to the proper operation of any music synthesizer. First be sure that diode deterioration is the cause of your trouble by measuring the voltage variation across the zener with a high-resistance voltmeter.

We will illustrate zener failure with two regulator circuits. The simplest is shown in Fig. 7-11. Here Q1 acts as an emitter follower to multiply the available current at a voltage determined primarily by the zener voltage of D3. In normal operation, three conditions can change the power supply output voltage:

(1) The voltage across the zener can affect the output because the current in the zener is not constant; as current demand at the regulated voltage increases, the rectified voltage drops, so less current will flow through the 1.5K resistor to maintain the zener voltage across D3.

(2) The current through the 47-ohm resistor is determined by the base current of Q1; Q1's base current, in turn, is determined by its emitter current, resulting in a slight change of voltage with load current.

(3) The drop from the Q1 base to emitter may not be constant with varying current.

If the zener fails, the voltage across it will rise, as will the output voltage at the emitter of Q1. Consequently, the output

180

becomes more dependent on load current. If the AC resistance of the zener increases, the regulation will deteriorate, but not so much.

The circuit of Fig. 7-12 is designed to provide better regulation because there is some regulation prior to the zener. The output voltage at the emitter of Q1 is compared with the zener voltage through a divider consisting of 1.2K, 5K, and 18K in series across the regulated supply (the 5K pot allows for output adjustment). This comparison determines the Q2 collector current which is drawn through 1K and 1.2K resistors from the raw rectified supply. This circuit does provide closer control of voltage with a varying load. As the load changes, the raw rectified voltage changes, so the Q2 collector current changes.

If D3 fails, Q2 stops conducting because its emitter has no return path. Regulation disappears, but the voltage may not rise as much as in the other circuit (Fig. 7-11), because Q2 takes only a relatively small bleeder current from the Q1 base. If D3's AC resistance increases, it will still deteriorate the regulation but not so much as in the simpler circuit.

A variation of voltage can be due to the failure of some component other than the zener reference that destroys the coupling between the zener reference and the voltage ultimately to be controlled. These possibilities are more varied due to the greater the number of components. The

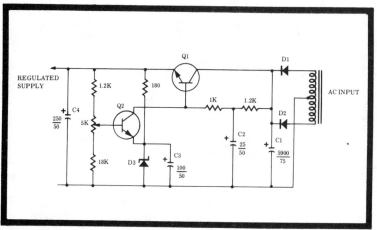

Fig. 7-12. A somewhat more sophisticated voltage regulator circuit with an adjustable output.

worst fault with either circuit is for Q1 to become either a short or open circuit, resulting in much higher or a complete loss of voltage respectively.

For the modular components in the synthesizer itself, if one becomes defective the procedure is to try interchange with similar available units. In any synthesizer there are a few kinds of units that do not at least have one duplicate in the system, thereby enabling a cross-check.

In conclusion, that fact that you picked up this book is an indication that you have a creative turn of mind and will undoubtedly find yourself getting deeper in the subject, one way or another. If your background is electronics, you will spread your interest into music, or further into it, if you were already interested in music. If your background is music, you will inevitably be dabbling in electronics before long, if you are not already. If you were just curious, you will want to get 'into' it, one way or another, sooner or later. So in all probability, one way or another, you will find yourself doing things you did not dream of earlier. You may add to the rapidly growing body of experience and knowledge in this fascinating and challenging subject. Good luck!

Chapter 8

Your Place In Electronic Music

Music always has been the meeting place between science and art, although not everyone recognizes the fact. The tempo of a musical beat involves arithmetical division of time into units. Pitch intervals involve an even more advanced study of mathematics. And the way conventional musical instruments derive the various pitches they play is another kind of mathematical study. But in modern times, traditionally, nobody seems to have compassed the whole gamut. Only exceptional men in history, like Leonardo da Vinci, seem to have accomplished that! Modern students are amazed at the variety of "disciplines" in which he was quite active. Really, it was not amazing at all. Look up the history of other men who were achievers in their own times: Pythagoras, Galileo, Newton, Edison, to name a few; everyone of them worked within a wide range of interests.

What these men possessed was an interest in the world around them. In their day, the various fields of interest were not so highly specialized. They did not know that anatomy would one day become the exclusive specialty of a profession called medical; that the study of the stars would be the field of astronomers; that the study of calculation would be the concern of mathematicians; or that a group of specialists called musicians and musicologists would devote their energies to a study of musical sounds.

Today, we tend to compartmentalize or exclusivize our thinking far too much. Because each of these different disciplines is the subject of intense specialization, we tend to think all of them are beyond us and, therefore, shrink from the challenge. This specialization process is almost reaching the ridiculous. For example, some physicians hesitate to enter the field of general practice, favoring instead the practice of a specialty. In many areas the old-fashioned general practitioner has no place.

Pursuing that analogy, with no intention to trespass on territory in which I am not licensed to practice, medicine has evidently reached a point where its practitioners are "standing in their own light." You may have a pain in the chest, for example, that is due to an abcess in your brain, pressing on a nerve that communicates with chest muscles. But for chest pains you go to a chest doctor: need I go on?

If you do not believe that, a personal experience may convince. Some years ago I actually had severe conjunctivitis of my right eye. It eventually proved to be due to pressure on a nerve in the dorsal region of my spine. As a result I finally lost sight in that eye, temporarily. Had I not gone to a chiropractor, the eye doctor would have removed my "infected" eye. Within an hour of the chiropractor's treatment, my sight was back and the pain diminishing rapidly. The doctor refused to believe this: the pain had been in my eye, not my spine!

Similarly, waveforms, frequencies, musical impressions conveyed to our sense of hearing, are all inseparably related in a quite complicated way. The musician knows what he hears but has no idea about waveforms, transistors as amplifying devices, and other components designed to process "signals," etc. And the audio engineer often does not appreciate music as a musician does because when he listens he does not hear music but a collection of sound waves.

An electronics devotee who gets himself into this world of "crazy people" will find himself about in the middle: talking to musicians, audio engineers, and a few other types, such as musicologists, each of whom has a few pet theories of his own about what makes what. To talk to them, we need to know some audio, some acoustics, some music, and the terms that go with each: in short to be a modern Leonardo da Vinci.

The exciting thing about the world these people live in is that they are creative. A service technician will not be creative, probably, so much as "fixative"! His job, traditionally, is to fix things that go wrong and to fix up the ideas the creative boys have, because they will know what they want to do but not how to do it. If that kind of activity sounds like a fun world for you to be in, it has plenty of room for you.

Repairing things that go wrong has been touched on specifically in the earlier chapters and treated with more depth in Chapter 7. Here, our objective is to help you orient

184

yourself to the kind of partnership you'll encounter as you move into the electronic music field. For, whether or not you have any formal partnership agreement, that is the position in which you'll find yourself.

If you enter the scene—any given scene—as a service technician you will know no more in general, possibly not as much of some specifics, as the people who call upon you for service or help. The reason they call upon you, believe it or not, is not for what you know but for your kind of know-how.

Much of the time, you may be facing some strange electronic "animal" that you have never seen before. But you know electronics and have a way of thinking your way through electronic problems, a capability that will make you invaluable to these people who call for your services. So, as I have said to many groups of people who were embarking on various new enterprises. "Do not be afraid of it!"

That is often the big deterrent: the feeling that you know nothing about this particular new "monster"; it looks so complicated; it has so many strange parts or units, etc.; you have no experience with it. What do all the parts do, or what are they supposed to do? Look on it as an adventure, because that is how your customer, client, or partner (according to how you view him) looks upon it. He would not be fooling with electronic music, otherwise.

So spend a little time getting to know your new partner "where he's at." Listen to some of the things he has done to familiarize yourself: he is bound to have recordings. Do not be afraid to ask how he achieved certain effects: he is itching to tell you, anyway. Not too many people are that interested: it is all beyond them, and they usually turn away rather than show their ignorance.

And if you still do not understand when he has told you, do not be afraid to ask more questions. This is your education and it could pay off handsomely later when you are regarded as an expert in the field. That is a pretty inexpensive and very effective way of acquiring an education! This book will have given you all the background to enable you to talk intelligently to these people.

Perhaps my own story of involvement in this field will help build your confidence. I never had a music lesson in my life. Somewhat over 10 years ago, a publisher asked if I could write a book on electronic organs. On occasion I had played with one a little, and I do know electronics fairly well (there were no transistors then) and the thing intrigued me. But surely someone else would know the subject better than I?

I suggested they would do better with an expert in the subject. Which was precisely what they were seeking. They convinced me that, with my background in writing electronic books, particularly first books of a kind or on a given subject, this made me the closest thing to an expert they were likely to find at that time. So I wrote the book.

Since then I have written several books on related subjects. Quite often now when I pick up a manufacturer's manual, if it has a bibliography of further reading, invariably there is at least one book of mine on the list, sometimes with some complimentary remarks about its value. Just that, apart from the royalties, makes it all worthwhile.

What this kind of thing takes—and you, if you are a serviceman in the field, are doing the same kind of thing—more than anything else, is the willingness to "have a go." Had I not written those books, I would probably not be writing this one. Certainly I would not as readily get the cooperation of everyone active in the electronic music business had I not done it. So you will have your niche in it, too.

Now, of course, being willing to try does not mean you are going to be stupid (although you will probably make your quota of mistakes that make you feel that way). For example, you know how easy it is to blow solid-state devices and how to handle them with care: be sure what you are doing before you prod anything or turn the power on with anything exposed. You know that it does not have dangerous voltages like the old tube equipment, that could give you a nasty jolt, but that the danger in this kind of equipment is to its components, not to you.

Listening to tapes or records of electronic music will help you to familiarize yourself with different kinds of sound; to listen for the kinds of sound that different electronic "tricks" can provide. Do you know the difference between the sound of a sine wave and that of a square wave, not to mention other waveforms used in synthesizers?

It does not take much practice, when you know what you are listening for, until you are able to identify the kind of tone produced by any given waveform. Waveforms do not sound sinusoidal, square, triangular or sawtooth, by analogy with those shapes, although you may eventually learn to associate them that way. What you hear and learn to identify are syntheses of fundamental and harmonics or overtones; or a basic note (fundamental) with a dominant coloration due to filtering.

This is how a musician (and you too, probably) can tell the difference between a clarinet, oboe, cornet, saxophone, etc. You recognize different waveforms (at least as they originated) in the same way: you hear what has been done to generate the sound to which you listen.

When something does not produce the kind of sound it should, the first step is to be sure how the objective is supposed to be achieved. Then discover why it fails. Often the sound will give you a good lead, or at least some clues.

For example, if a synthesizer tone is supposed to be sinusoidal, which is a pure, somewhat weak sounding tone, and the one you hear is obviously rich in harmonics, more like a square wave, you know something is wrong. First you find out how the sine wave is supposed to be generated. If it uses a basic sine-wave generator, excessive feedback or coupling will cause the oscillator to work too hard, yielding a highly distorted waveform. You then look for what went wrong with the feedback or coupling.

But if it uses a function generator approach, the generator probably starts with a triangular wave that should be converted to a sinusoidal form by shaping. The waveshaper may have gone out of action or it may be working incorrectly, somehow. Or maybe the amplitude control has "let loose" so the shaper does not have the correct input.

If you have difficulty getting into the generator (due to its physical construction) you may want to try to diagnose the trouble before you get inside to start checking. So you will observe whether the pitch shifts from what it is supposed to be, in addition to the waveform being wrong.

In a sine-wave generator with excessive coupling, the pitch almost certainly shifts a little from the correct pitch. If it does not, the cause of distortion probably is in a later stage and the generator could be OK. The direction of shift also may tell you something, whether it is up or down in frequency. You look for component changes or defects that would shift the frequency in the direction it has taken, as well as increase the coupling or feedback.

With a function generator, if the amplitude control goes out of action the period increases, lowering the frequency for sure. If the frequency stays put, the shaper is more likely at fault. This is the kind of logic that helps trace troubles in such unfamiliar kinds of equipment.

As well as tracing faults, putting things right that go wrong, in this kind of business you will almost certainly be asked to innovate. Your musician friends will hear some new sound and want it. "How can I get that?" they will ask you. They may think they know what it takes, and they may be quite wrong! For example, from a musical point of view, the "new sound" may be a bit like one thing they have heard before and a bit like something else. So the musician may jump to the conclusion that the new sound is made by combining those two things electronically. Logical enough, if he does not know electronics!

With your knowledge of electronics, you may realize that particular combination is not possible or that it would not produce the result your friend thinks it would. In this kind of situation, you should try to hear the "new sound," too. While the musician is listening for musical effect, you will listen with an ear trained to determine what happens to the waveform.

Be careful. You can soon sink a lot of time in this kind of work. Lots of people have thought they could build an electronic organ to save money over buying one. The only way this will work is if you buy a kit: you save on the assembly labor. But if you buy the parts piecemeal and try to put an organ together, you will pay more for the parts than a whole organ would cost, and you still have to build it and, hopefully, make it work.

The same goes for experimenting with other electronic instruments. Do not do it to save money: you will not! But if you do it to experiment, that is fine. You may just learn something that will put you ahead of the game. Even in that, let me caution you. Do you have marketing facilities, or someone who is so equipped with whom you could build up a business? Because if you do not, all you will probably do is end up building one of a kind, at a rather inordinately high cost. I would not say that you may not find it worth the effort: that is for you to decide; I am just warning you!

Index